Linear Programming for Project Management Professionals

Explore Concepts, Techniques, and Tools to Achieve Project Management Objectives

Partha Majumdar

www.bpbonline.com

FIRST EDITION 2022
Copyright © BPB Publications, India
ISBN: 978-93-55511-164

LIMITS OF LIABILITY AND DISCLAIMER OF WARRANTY

To View Complete
BPB Publications Catalogue
Scan the QR Code:

Dedicated to

Our dear daughters

Riya

&

Ranoo

About the Author

Partha Majumdar is just a programmer. He has been involved in developing more than 10 Enterprise Class products that have been deployed in customer locations in more than 57 countries. He has worked with key ministries of 8 countries in developing key systems for them. Also, he has been involved in the development of key systems for more than 20 enterprises.

Partha has been employed in enterprises including Siemens, Amdocs, NIIT, Mobily, JP Morgan Chase & Co. Apart from developing systems in the companies, Partha managed highly profitable business units. He has set up 3 reasonably successful companies as of 2021 in India, Dubai, and Saudi Arabia.

Partha has worked on developing OLTP systems for Telcos, Hospitals, Tea Gardens, Insurance Companies, Travel Houses, Cricket Tournaments, etc. Since 2012, Partha has been developing Data Products and has been intensively working on Machine Learning and Deep Learning.

Partha has continued to learn new domains and technology throughout his career. After his graduation in Mathematics, Partha has completed a Master's in Telecommunications and Computer Security. He has completed executive MBAs in Information Systems and Business Analytics. He recently completed the PG Certificate program in AI/ML/DL from Manipal Academy of Higher Education, Dubai, and advanced certificate in Cyber Security from IIT, Kanpur. He is currently pursuing advanced certificate in Computational Data Sciences from IISc, Bangalore.

Partha is an avid traveler. He has had the opportunity to visit 32 countries for work and leisure so far.

Partha is married to Deepshree and has 2 daughters - Riya and Ranoo.

About the Reviewers

❖ **Dr. Anand Handa** is working as a Senior Project Executive Officer at C3i Center, IIT Kanpur. His focus areas include malware analysis, memory forensics, intrusion detection systems, and computer vision. His role at the C3i Center involves working on malware analysis projects, IDS as a significant component with machine learning at its intersection. He is a member of the IET - Cybersecurity working group and Bureau of Indian Standards (BIS -- IoT Security and Privacy Panel).

❖ An Electronics and Communication Engineer by Profession, **Tulika Pandey** currently holds the position of Sr. Director, Cyber Security Group with the Ministry of Electronics & Information Technology. She has 29 years of professional experience as Team Lead of National and International initiatives of Government of India be it Research & Development, Policy, Regulation or Strategy Formulation in the areas of Governance, Information & Communication Technologies and Cyber Security. She has acquired certifications in Intellectual Property Rights Law from ILI, New Delhi, Cyber Security & Cyber Defense from IIT Kanpur, and Internet Governance from the University of Malta. She is a member of a few Technical Societies and Committees, notable are - International Advisory Board of the International Conference on "COMmunication System & NETworkS (COMSNETS)", Standards for Telecom Equipments of the Telecom Engineering Centre (TEC, Dept. of Telecommunications, Govt. of India), Member of Institution of Engineer & Telecommunication Engineer (IETE). As a member of the United Nations 'Internet Governance Forum,' she was instrumental in establishing the Indian Chapter of Internet Governance Forum (IIGF), India.

Acknowledgement

First and foremost, I would like to thank my parents for continuously encouraging me for writing books.

Then, I would like to thank Deepshree, who was the first reader of the book. She is an Electronics Engineer and has mainly been in operations and has no experience in project management. She agreed to run through all the contents in the book and this helped me test whether people with no prior background in project management could understand this book.

I am grateful to all the companies where I have worked. All the contents in this book have been collated from experiences I have gathered from the different projects I have been assigned by NIIT Ltd, Siemens Information Systems Ltd, and Mobily.

My extreme gratitude goes to BPB Publications team for being so thorough in the review of the book and for being enormously supportive at every step of the development of the book.

Preface

The book covers a different aspect of Project Scheduling. Project Scheduling mainly deals with the aspect of time involved in conducting a project. However, we will explore in the book that Project Scheduling cannot be successfully conducted without paying attention to the dimensions of costs involved in a project and the scope to be delivered by a project.

The techniques discussed in the book are essential to understand by anyone involved with a project. More so, the Project Managers or Program Managers need to be aware of these concepts. This book shows the implementation of the concepts using Microsoft Excel. Many of the concepts discussed in the book are not possible to implement using popular project management tools like Microsoft Project, Primavera, etc.

The book starts with a discussion on project scheduling in **chapter 1.** As we need the WBS for scheduling a project, we discuss the methods for creating a WBS. Then we proceed to discuss PDM. We round up the chapter with the PDM being formulated in an MS Excel sheet and by identifying the critical path of a project.

In **chapter 2**, we discuss methods of monitoring a project using EVM. We discuss how to estimate the project cost. Once the project cost is established, the indicators to monitor the project is discussed.

In **chapter 3**, LPP is discussed. The chapter describes the need for optimization. The chapter explains the mathematical basis for the formulation of an LPP. The discussion is then moved to ways of solving the LPP using the graphical method. The limitation of the graphical method is discussed and the need for a tool like Solver of MS Excel is established. The chapter explains how LPP can be solved using Solver.

In **chapter 4**, we start our discussion on crashing a project. First, we discuss what is crashing a project. The theory behind crashing a project is explained. We discuss the rules for crashing a project. And we establish a method for crashing a project.

In **chapter 5**, the problem of crashing a project is formulated as an LPP. The chapter discusses how the LPP can be solved using Solver.

In **chapter 6**, more complex problems of crashing a project are discussed.

In **chapter 7**, we discuss how EVM can be linked with the problem of crashing a project.

The readers are assumed to be conversant with the use of MS Excel. However, in case readers use some other spreadsheet or for whatever reason are not aware of MS Excel, an introduction to MS Excel has been included as an annexure.

A second annexure has been included to discuss advanced techniques of crashing a project.

Coloured Images

Please follow the link to download the
Coloured Images of the book:

https://rebrand.ly/83995b

We have code bundles from our rich catalogue of books and videos available at **https://github.com/bpbpublications**. Check them out!

Errata

We take immense pride in our work at BPB Publications and follow best practices to ensure the accuracy of our content to provide with an indulging reading experience to our subscribers. Our readers are our mirrors, and we use their inputs to reflect and improve upon human errors, if any, that may have occurred during the publishing processes involved. To let us maintain the quality and help us reach out to any readers who might be having difficulties due to any unforeseen errors, please write to us at :

errata@bpbonline.com

Your support, suggestions and feedbacks are highly appreciated by the BPB Publications' Family.

Did you know that BPB offers eBook versions of every book published, with PDF and ePub files available? You can upgrade to the eBook version at www.bpbonline.com and as a print book customer, you are entitled to a discount on the eBook copy. Get in touch with us at :

business@bpbonline.com for more details.

At **www.bpbonline.com**, you can also read a collection of free technical articles, sign up for a range of free newsletters, and receive exclusive discounts and offers on BPB books and eBooks.

Piracy

If you come across any illegal copies of our works in any form on the internet, we would be grateful if you would provide us with the location address or website name. Please contact us at **business@bpbonline.com** with a link to the material.

If you are interested in becoming an author

If there is a topic that you have expertise in, and you are interested in either writing or contributing to a book, please visit **www.bpbonline.com**. We have worked with thousands of developers and tech professionals, just like you, to help them share their insights with the global tech community. You can make a general application, apply for a specific hot topic that we are recruiting an author for, or submit your own idea.

Reviews

Please leave a review. Once you have read and used this book, why not leave a review on the site that you purchased it from? Potential readers can then see and use your unbiased opinion to make purchase decisions. We at BPB can understand what you think about our products, and our authors can see your feedback on their book. Thank you!

For more information about BPB, please visit **www.bpbonline.com**.

Table of Contents

CHAPTER 1
Project Scheduling

Welcome to this book!!!

This book aims to help readers create optimized project schedules from the perspective of both time and cost. So, we will start with the nuances of creating a project schedule.

We need to have a project before we can discuss the project schedule. I will state an imaginary project with all the real elements that a project needs to have. Using this as an example, we will break down the scope of the project into several components and organize these components to create the **Work Breakdown Structure (WBS)**. Once we have the WBS, we can start our discussion on scheduling the project.

We will use the **Precedence Diagramming Method (PDM)** for scheduling the project. We will discuss the different elements of PDM in this chapter. And we will put all these elements together to arrive at the project schedule at the end.

Let's drive the discussion through an example. Then, you can replace the example with your real case and arrive at the desired project schedule for your project.

The techniques discussed in this book can be applied to any project in any industry, but we shall take up examples from software engineering projects.

Structure

We will discuss the following topics in this chapter:

- Our project

- **Section 1:** Project Scheduling theory
  - Work Breakdown Structure (WBS)
    - One method of creating the WBS
    - Planting the WBS on Microsoft Excel
  - Estimating the duration for each task in the WBS
  - Sequencing the tasks in the WBS
    - Relationship between the tasks
    - Lags between the tasks
    - Creating the task sequence
  - Creating the project network
  - Calculating the project duration
    - Conducting the forward pass
    - Conducting the backward pass
  - Calculating slack for each task
  - Determining the critical path

- **Section 2:** Excel Implementation
  - Calculating ES, EF, LS, and LF using Microsoft Excel
    - Conducting the forward pass
    - Conducting the backward pass
    - Calculating the Slack for each task

Objectives

After going through this chapter, you should be able to create a **Work Breakdown Structure (WBS)** for a project and estimate the duration for each task in the WBS.

You will understand the relationships between the tasks. You will learn what Lag is, how to create the project network using **Precedence Diagramming Method (PDM)**, and how to calculate the project duration. You will also understand early start, early finish, late start, late finish, critical path, and what slack is.

Implementing a project on new library management system

To start the discussion, let's take up a project. Using this project as our example, we will see how we can arrive at a schedule for a project.

Let's consider that we have a project for implementing a new library management system for a university.

Once the project is assigned to a project manager, the project manager's first task is to understand the various elements. They must get a firm idea of the scope of the project, the budget, and the time to complete it. Cost, scope, and schedule are the three pillars of any project. The project manager should manage these three pillars to ensure that the project delivers the product with the desired quality. These pillars undergo changes while the project is in execution, but a project manager should maintain a balance between them so that the project progresses toward creating a quality product.

This book focuses on the schedule aspect of the project, but it will become increasingly clear as we progress that we cannot discuss schedules in isolation. We will have to discuss cost and scope as well. For now, we will assume that the scope of the project remains constant (though this is never the case in a real-life situation). As far as the cost is concerned, we cannot isolate it under any circumstances as schedule and cost go hand in hand. As they say, time is money.

We generally have a high-level understanding of the scope at the start of any project. Sales teams aim to make the scope as tight as possible before the contract is signed. However, it is almost always the case that new activities surface once project execution starts. This is not due to the sales team's lack of skills but because of changes in the project parameters over time. Some of the assumptions become invalid and new realities emerge, so a different set of skills are needed to manage the scope of the project.

Let's assume that the scope is as follows for our project to implement a new library management system:

- We need to buy the required hardware to implement the software
- We need to buy the software that will be implemented
- We need to customize the software so that all the needs of the university are fulfilled
- Once the software is ready, we need to migrate the data from the existing system to the new system
- And lastly, we need to roll out the new software

Section - I
Project
Scheduling Theory

Let us first go through the theory related to project scheduling. Once we have understood the theory, we will implement the calculations in Microsoft Excel in the section 2.

Work breakdown structure

Once the scope of the project is clear, we need to identify all the tasks that are to be conducted to complete the project. The process of identifying all the tasks for a project and arranging them systematically is known as the process of creating the WBS.

There are several ways to build the WBS, but all the methods can be classified into two approaches to create the WBS, i.e., we either build it using the **Top-Down** approach or the **Bottom-Up** approach.

In the top-down approach for preparing the WBS, we start from the project and break it down into component tasks. We again break the component tasks into smaller component tasks till we reach a point where we no longer need to break the task.

> **Note:** As a guideline, we should break a task into component tasks till we reach a point where a task can be assigned to an individual.This mechanism is important because in a project, we should make individuals accountable for the tasks they perform. It also allows for measuring the efficiency of the individuals.

The top-down approach for preparing the WBS is the most suitable in software development projects. In a software development project, we would try to find the main components to develop and then break each component into subcomponents. We would continue the task of decomposition until individual components that need development (typically, these were program units to develop) were identified. We would have tasks for each leaf-level component (typically, a program to be written or tested), for writing the program, testing the component, and so on.

In the bottom-up approach for preparing the WBS, we would collect all the tasks that we need to perform in the project and group the tasks into logical sets. We would keep moving up by creating logical sets till we have the project as the task.

I used the bottom-up approach for preparing the WBS when I executed a project for resource augmentation for one of our customers. During this project, the profiles of resources to be supplied to the customer were clear at the beginning. For each profile, it was clear how many candidates we would need, and we were also clear regarding the tasks to be performed for each candidate. The typical tasks included advertising on LinkedIn and other social media, interviewing the candidate, sending job offers, getting visa applications filled, applying for visa, getting flight tickets, getting medical insurance, and so on. As you can see, we could group the tasks logically; for example, applying for a visa for all the candidates could be grouped in one set. Further, all the tasks for applying for visa, getting the air tickets, getting the medical insurance, and so on could be grouped as on-boarding tasks.

Creating the WBS

Let's discuss one method of creating the WBS using the top-down approach. This method is general and can be applied for most types of projects.

For any project, we need to have a process for *initiating the project*. Typically, the project manager would be assigned in this process. It also involves other activities like registering the project in the books of finance, setting up the project in the **Project Management Office** (**PMO**), and such. We will consider that we are creating the WBS from the point where the project manager has taken over the project.

After any project has been initiated, there is a phase where it is be planned. We will call this phase the *Project Planning Phase*.

The project will enter the *Execution Phase* once it has been planned. While the project is being executed, we will have a parallel process for *Monitoring and Control*. Lastly, we will have a process for *Closing the Project* when it is complete.

So, we can create five sub-tasks for our project, as shown in *figure 1.1*:

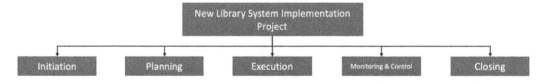

Figure 1.1: *WBS - First level of decomposition*

Next, we need to break down these top-level tasks into component tasks. We will break down the tasks to one more level. We will not proceed in this discussion as further decomposition will be specific to a project.

Let's start with the *initiation* task. Generally, we will at least perform the following activities during project initiation:

1. Conduct a kick-off meeting

2. Prepare the project charter

3. Sign-off the project charter

Let's say that we also include the following tasks to be conducted for this project during the *project initiation phase*:

- Identify the hardware

- Identify the software

Now, our WBS will look as displayed in *figure 1.2*:

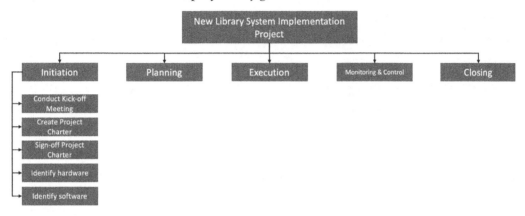

Figure 1.2: *WBS - Initiation task decomposed*

Next, let's decompose the **Planning** task. During the planning phase, the tasks will vary from one organization to another and one project to another. However, the following tasks are always conducted during planning:

1. Create the project plan

2. Create the project schedule

3. Identify project team

4. Allocate budgets

5. Sign-off the project plan

Note: Information regarding the project schedule, project team, project budgets, etc. is included in the project plan, in addition to the information about the scope, risks, and such. Also, project plans include strategies for scope management, configuration management, risk management, communication management, quality management, and much more.

For our discussion, let's say that we only have the above mentioned five tasks for the planning phase. So, our WBS will look as shown in *figure 1.3*. One could also consider creating the project schedule, identifying the project team, and allocating budgets as sub-tasks of creating the project plan. We will keep it simple for the moment.

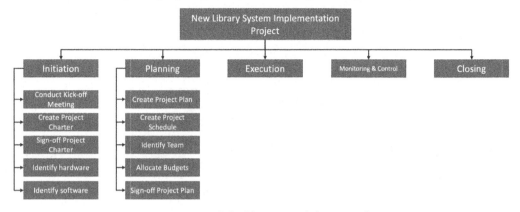

Figure 1.3: WBS - Planning task decomposed

Let's decompose the **Execution** task next. The tasks in the execution phase are specific to a project in most cases. Similar projects will have similar tasks in the execution phase. On many occasions, we will use the tasks in the execution phase of a similar project as a template for a new project. However, there must be some unique tasks during the execution of every project. This is simply because every project is unique and, by definition, every project produces something unique.

Let's consider that we have the following tasks in our project for implementing a new library management system:

1. Purchase hardware

2. Purchase software

3. Install hardware

4. Create prototype

5. Sign-off prototype

6. Customize software

7. Sign-off software

8. Conduct data migration

9. Sign-off implementation

10. Go live

So, our WBS would look as shown in *figure 1.4*:

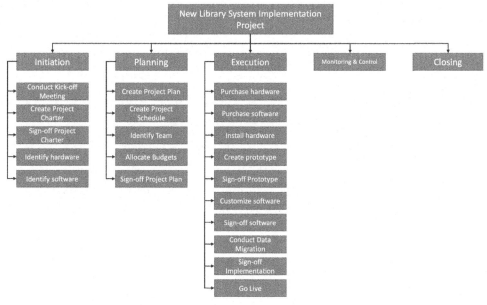

Figure 1.4: *WBS - Execution task decomposed*

The high-level tasks in the **Monitoring and Control** process are generally the same in every project. However, specific tasks are designed by big companies as per their processes. *Figure 1.5* shows the tasks that come under **Monitoring and Control**.

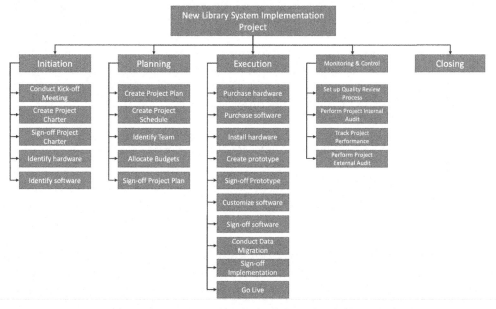

Figure 1.5: *WBS - Monitoring and Control task decomposed*

Projects will usually have similar tasks in the **Project Closing Phase** . However, there can be specific tasks as per every organization's process. Let's take a look at the tasks in the **Project Closing Phase**, as shown in *figure 1.6*:

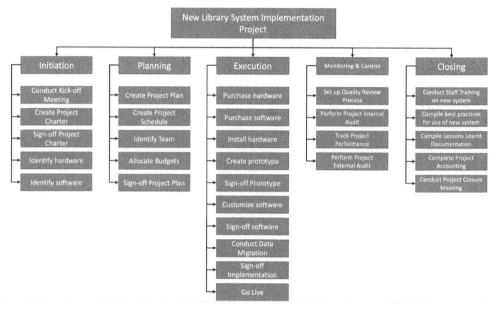

Figure 1.6: WBS - Closing task decomposed

So, now we have a WBS. This can be a reasonable WBS at the start of the project. In all probabilities, each task will be further decomposed into subtasks when project execution starts.

> **Note:** Every task in a project that involves getting a sign-off needs to be considered as a separate task. Though getting a sign-off seems like a milestone in a project, these tasks can consume a lot of time and effort. This is especially true when the sign-off must be obtained from the customer.

Planting the WBS on a Microsoft Excel sheet

Next, we will plant the WBS on a Microsoft Excel sheet. In this book, we have considered Microsoft Excel for project scheduling. Later in the book, we will conduct activities on the project schedule that are not possible using popular tools like *Microsoft Project, Primavera,* and such.

> **Note:** Every reader of this book may not know how to use Microsoft Excel, so a chapter on Microsoft Excel is included in the appendix of the book. I would suggest readers who are unfamiliar with Microsoft Excel to go through that chapter now.

The WBS created using *Microsoft Excel* is as shown in *figure 1.7*:

	A	B
1	**Task ID**	**Task Description**
2	A	Initiation
3	A.1	Conduct Kick-off Meeting
4	A.2	Create Project Charter
5	A.3	Sign-off Project Charter
6	A.4	Identify Hardware
7	A.5	Identify Software
8	B	Planning
9	B.1	Create Project Plan
10	B.2	Create Project Schedule
11	B.3	Identify Team
12	B.4	Allocate Budget
13	B.5	Sign-off Project Plan
14	C	Execution
15	C.1	Purchase Hardware
16	C.2	Purchase Software
17	C.3	Install Hardware
18	C.4	Create Prototype
19	C.5	Sign-off Prototype
20	C.6	Customise Software
21	C.7	Sign-off Software
22	C.8	Conduct Data Migration
23	C.9	Sign-off Implementation
24	C.10	Go Live
25	D	Monitoring & Control
26	D.1	Set up Quality Review Process
27	D.2	Perform Project Internal Audit
28	D.3	Track Project Performance
29	D.4	Perform Project External Audit
30	E	Closing
31	E.1	Conduct Staff Training on New System
32	E.2	Compile Best Practices for use of New System
33	E.3	Compile Lessons Learnt Document
34	E.4	Complete Project Accounting
35	E.5	Conduct Project Closure Meeting

Figure 1.7: *WBS planted on Microsoft Excel*

Estimating the duration of tasks in the WBS

Once we have the WBS, we need to estimate the time required for conducting each task. There are many methods for estimating the duration of a task; a book can be written on the different techniques. For this book, we need the duration of tasks for the purpose of project scheduling, so we will only consider two commonly used techniques for estimating the time required to execute each task in the project.

The most prevalent technique for estimating the project duration is to assign all tasks to a prospective team member and seek their opinion regarding the amount of time required to execute the tasks. This may sound ancient, but every team adopts this technique.

So, we will start from the leaf level tasks in the WBS and get the estimate for the time required for all the tasks. Then, we will collate all these durations to arrive at the time required for all the higher-level tasks. The subject matter experts are asked to provide this estimate when the project team is not fully formed or when the project team members assigned to tasks are relatively new to the task. There are occasions when the project manager uses their judgment to arrive at the estimates. These judgments may be based on the experience of having completed similar tasks for some other project.

Note: When a project manager, subject matter expert, or any other project resource uses experience for estimating the duration of a task, we refer to it as using the Analogous Estimation method. In the *Analogous Estimation* method, a similar project from the past is picked up and small adjustments are made to the estimates of that project based on the uniqueness of the current project to arrive at the final estimate for the current project.Another method of using historical data for estimation is called the *Parametric Estimation* method. An example for the same is provided in *figure 1.8*.

Parameter	A \# Included in Estimate	B Rating Factor	C Complexity Adjustment	Estimate (A*B*C)	Comments
Parametric Estimate					
Environment					
New URL	1.00	10.00	1.60	16.00	Moving from Traditional to AWS
New Web Site	1.00	5.00	1.00	5.00	Existing Website being replatformed and enriched
New Instance of Environment/New Server	5.00	15.00	1.80	135.00	Will need including factors like VPNs, Security, etc
Style Sheet Modifications	20.00	3.00	0.75	45.00	New design to be incorporated
Subtotal				**201.00**	
New Pages					
Page Creation – per page	20.00	3.00	0.90	54.00	Existing code to be reused + Programming to be done on templates and thus lot of resue
New Data Fields – per 25 fields	7.00	2.00	1.00	14.00	Mainly planting on HTML + Validation Rules
Changes to Existing Pages					
Straight html	40.00	0.50	0.40	8.00	Minor modifications + Application of new Style Sheets
Field changes	60.00	1.00	1.10	66.00	New Validation Rules + Back end changes + DB Changes + SQL changes
Subtotal				**142.00**	
Database					
New Table	10.00	0.50	0.90	4.50	Includes design
Add fields to or alter existing table	20.00	0.25	0.40	2.00	Mainly implementation
New stored procedure	40.00	5.00	1.30	260.00	Mainly business rules related
Change existing stored procedure	50.00	2.50	0.50	62.50	Mainly due to changes in DB Design
Database (data) fix	60.00	1.00	1.20	72.00	Migrating data to changed structure
Constraint changes	100.00	0.50	0.60	30.00	Assuming DBMS not changed
Add new index	100.00	0.50	0.60	30.00	Assuming DBMS not changed
Subtotal				**461.00**	

Figure 1.8: Example of parametric estimate

A slightly more sophisticated technique for estimating the duration of a task is to get at least three estimates for the task from different resources. We will then classify the estimates into three categories: optimistic estimate, most probable estimate, and pessimistic estimate. If we get more than one estimate for either of these, we can take their mean to arrive at the respective estimate.

Now, we will have three estimates for each task. Let's represent the optimistic estimate as O, most probable estimate as M, and pessimistic estimate as P. Then, we will compute the duration for the task using the following formula:

Task Duration Estimate = (O + 4M + P) / 6

This method of task duration estimation is called the **3-point estimation technique**. Two formulae are popular in 3-point estimation techniques. When we use the *(O + M + P)/3* formula to estimate the task duration, we use the **Triangular Distribution**. When we use the *(O + 4M + P)/6* formula, we use the **Beta Distribution**. The beta distribution formula is generally used for 3-point estimation.

Suppose we have a WBS containing 15 tasks named A through O, and the optimistic, most probable, and pessimistic estimates of each task are as shown in *figure 1.9*. Then, we can calculate the estimated duration for each task using the beta distribution formula of 3-point estimation, as shown in *figure 1.9*:

Activity	Optimistic (O)	Most Probable (M)	Pessimistic (P)	Expected = (O+4M+P)/6	Estimate = Round(Expected)	Standard Deviation = (P - O)/6
A	1	2	4	2.166666667	2	0.50
B	2	3	4	3	3	0.33
C	5	6	8	6.166666667	6	0.50
D	3	4	6	4.166666667	4	0.50
E	2	3	4	3	3	0.33
F	3	5	6	4.833333333	5	0.50
G	4	5	6	5	5	0.33
H	5	6	8	6.166666667	6	0.50
I	2	3	5	3.166666667	3	0.50
J	6	7	9	7.166666667	7	0.50
K	4	5	6	5	5	0.33
L	2	3	5	3.166666667	3	0.50
M	4	5	7	5.166666667	5	0.50
N	6	7	9	7.166666667	7	0.50
O	1	1	1	1	1	0.00

Figure 1.9: Example of 3-point estimation

Let's assume that we have obtained the duration for each task in our WBS using an appropriate technique, and the estimates are as shown in *figure 1.10*. The duration would be in units like hours, days, weeks, months, or years.

	A	B	C
1	Task ID	Task Description	Duration
2	A	Initiation	
3	A.1	Conduct Kick-off Meeting	1
4	A.2	Create Project Charter	5
5	A.3	Sign-off Project Charter	2
6	A.4	Identify Hardware	6
7	A.5	Identify Software	8
8	B	Planning	
9	B.1	Create Project Plan	4
10	B.2	Create Project Schedule	2
11	B.3	Identify Team	2
12	B.4	Allocate Budget	2
13	B.5	Sign-off Project Plan	3
14	C	Execution	
15	C.1	Purchase Hardware	15
16	C.2	Purchase Software	15
17	C.3	Install Hardware	10
18	C.4	Create Prototype	20
19	C.5	Sign-off Prototype	3
20	C.6	Customise Software	90
21	C.7	Sign-off Software	10
22	C.8	Conduct Data Migration	60
23	C.9	Sign-off Implementation	10
24	C.10	Go Live	5
25	D	Monitoring & Control	
26	D.1	Set up Quality Review Process	3
27	D.2	Perform Project Internal Audit	15
28	D.3	Track Project Performance	20
29	D.4	Perform Project External Audit	3
30	E	Closing	
31	E.1	Conduct Staff Training on New System	8
32	E.2	Compile Best Practices for use of New System	5
33	E.3	Compile Lessons Learnt Document	3
34	E.4	Complete Project Accounting	5
35	E.5	Conduct Project Closure Meeting	1

Figure 1.10: *WBS updated with the duration for each task*

Sequencing the tasks in the WBS

The next step is to logically sequence the tasks in the order that they can be performed. The sequence of the tasks will depend on their nature as some tasks may require other tasks to be completed before they can start, or sequencing may be required due to some constraints. For example, a lack of resources may cause us to be unable to start a task before some other tasks are completed and the resources are available.

To sequence the tasks, we define the predecessors for each task. A task that does not have a predecessor can be started any time in the project. A task that has a predecessor can be started only as per the rules of the relationship. Now we will discuss the different types of possible relationships between the tasks.

Relationships between the tasks

When we sequence the tasks, we build a relationship between them. There are four possible relationships between tasks. Let's discuss these relationships before proceeding further.

For the rest of the discussion in this section, we will consider two tasks named A and B. Task A is the predecessor of task B. We will define the relationship between these two tasks. In *Microsoft Excel*, we will formulate this as shown in *figure 1.11*:

Task ID	Duration	Predecessor
A	5	
B	4	A

Figure 1.11: Predecessor defined for task B

Finish-to-start relationship

The first task must be completed before the next task can start in the finish-to-start relationship. This is the default relationship between the two tasks. In software like *Microsoft Project*, defining only the predecessor for a task with no qualifiers means that the relationship is finish-to-start. As can be seen in *figure 1.11*, the predecessor for task B is task A. There is no qualifier, so it means the relationship between task A and task B is a finish-to-start relationship. This means task B can start only after task A has been completed.

We can make the relationship explicit by adding the suffix FS, as shown in *figure 1.12*:

Task ID	Duration	Predecessor
A	5	
B	4	A FS

Figure 1.12: Making finish-to-start relationship explicit

Diagrammatically, the finish-to-start relationship is represented as follows:

Figure 1.13: Diagrammatic representation of finish-to-start relationship

The tasks are represented by the rectangles, inside which we write the task ID. We write the duration of the task within the orange colored ellipse inside the rectangle.

There are lots of examples of tasks where we apply finish-to-start relationships. Suppose you are traveling by air. If we have two tasks—one for checking in and one for clearing the security check—we can proceed for the security check only after we have completed checking in.

In software development, suppose we have two tasks: one for developing a unit and one for testing the unit. Generally, we can test a unit only after its development has been completed. We will discuss some exceptions for this later in the chapter.

Finish-to-finish relationship

In the finish-to-finish relationship, the two tasks in relation to each other must be completed together no matter when they have started. We can also understand this as task B cannot finish until task A completes. This type of relationship is represented by adding an FF in the predecessor column, as shown in *figure 1.14*:

Task ID	Duration	Predecessor
A	5	
B	4	A FF

Figure 1.14: Coding finish-to-finish relationship

Diagrammatically, we can represent the finish-to-finish relationship as shown in *figure 1.15*:

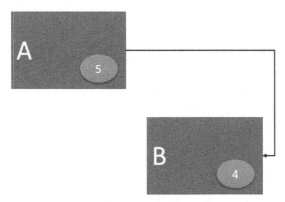

Figure 1.15: Diagrammatic representation of finish-to-finish relationship

We find this type of relationship frequently in many jobs. Suppose we have a task to gather the requirements for a project and another task to design the product based on the gathered requirements. Now, we may start the job of designing before all the requirements have been gathered. However, the task of designing the system cannot be completed till all the requirements have been gathered.

In the construction industry, we can find another example for this type of relationship between tasks. A pipe can be insulated once it is installed. The job of installing a pipe and insulating a pipe can proceed simultaneously, but the task of insulating a pipe cannot be completed until the task of installing the pipe is completed.

Take another example. Suppose we have two tasks of washing the dishes and drying the dishes. Now, the tasks of washing the dishes and drying the dishes can proceed together, but the task of drying the dishes cannot be completed till the task of washing the dishes is completed.

Start-to-start relationship

In a start-to-start relationship, the two tasks in relation to each other must start simultaneously. We can also understand this as task B cannot start until task A starts. In other words, B can start when A starts. This type of relationship is represented by adding an SS in the predecessor column, as shown in *figure 1.16*:

Task ID	Duration	Predecessor
A	5	
B	4	A SS

Figure 1.16: Coding start-to-start relationship

In software product development, we can start testing the system once the process of customization of the system has started. Clearly, we cannot start testing before the customization process has started. Also, testing does not have to start as soon as the customization process starts.

Diagrammatically, we can represent the start-to-start relationship as shown in *figure 1.17*:

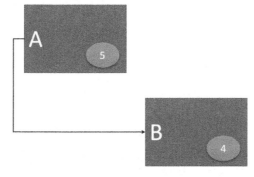

Figure 1.17: Diagrammatic representation of start-to-start relationship

Start-to-finish relationship

Start-to-finish is rare, and many pundits consider this relationship unnecessary.

In the start-to-finish relationship, task A must start before the preceding task—task B—can finish. In other words, task B will continue till task A starts. This type of relationship is represented by adding an SF in the predecessor column, as shown in *figure 1.18*:

Task ID	Duration	Predecessor
A	5	
B	4	A SF

Figure 1.18: *Coding start-to-finish relationship*

Diagrammatically, we can represent the start-to-finish relationship as shown in *figure 1.19*:

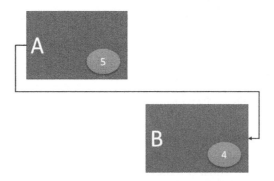

Figure 1.19: *Diagrammatic representation of start-to-finish relationship*

As an example, we can consider that we have two tasks during software development: one for continuous revisions and improvements and another for program testing. Now, the task of continuous revisions and improvements continues until the task of program testing starts. The start of program testing ends the task of continuous revisions and improvements to the software.

Lags between the tasks

We need to discuss the concept of lags before proceeding to sequence our tasks. In the previous section, we discussed the different possible relations between tasks. For example, we have a finish-to-start relationship between two tasks. Let's say that the tasks are for developing a unit of software and testing that unit of software. Now, the project manager decides that the testing will start 3 days after the development has completed. There can be reasons for such a decision, for instance, the testing team may be a different entity, and the project manager may have to allot a particular amount of time as lead time to such a unit.

In this situation, we say that we are adding a lag of 3 days. We represent this as shown in *figure 1.20*:

Task ID	Duration	Predecessor
A	5	
B	4	A FS+3d

Figure 1.20: Finish-to-start relationship with lag

Now, lag need not always be a positive number; it can be a negative number as well. Let's consider our previous example of having two tasks: one for developing a piece of software and another for testing that piece of software. The project manager may decide that software testing will start 5 days before the completion of the development of the software. This is a common practice. When we see that the software is about 80% ready, we start testing the software while the rest of the software is still being developed.

Under the above-mentioned circumstances, we say that there is a lag of -5 days between the task of development of the software and the task of testing the software. We represent this, as shown in *figure 1.21*:

Task ID	Duration	Predecessor
A	40	
B	8	A FS-5d

Figure 1.21: Finish-to-start relationship with negative lag

Creating the task sequence

Now that we have discussed the different types of possible relationships between the tasks, let's sequence the tasks in our project. Let's set the relations between the tasks as shown in *figure 1.22*. You can also set the relations as per your understanding. The relationships between the tasks may be different even in two identical projects.

	A	B	C	D
1	Task ID	Task Description	Duration	Predecessor
2	A	Initiation		
3	A.1	Conduct Kick-off Meeting	1	
4	A.2	Create Project Charter	5	
5	A.3	Sign-off Project Charter	2	A.2
6	A.4	Identify Hardware	6	A.1,A.3
7	A.5	Identify Software	8	A.1,A.3
8	B	Planning		
9	B.1	Create Project Plan	4	A.3
10	B.2	Create Project Schedule	2	B.1
11	B.3	Identify Team	2	B.1
12	B.4	Allocate Budget	2	B.1,A.4,A.5
13	B.5	Sign-off Project Plan	3	B.2,B.3,B.4
14	C	Execution		
15	C.1	Purchase Hardware	15	A.4,B.5
16	C.2	Purchase Software	15	A.5,B.5
17	C.3	Install Hardware	10	C.1
18	C.4	Create Prototype	20	C.2,C.3 FS+2
19	C.5	Sign-off Prototype	3	C.4
20	C.6	Customise Software	90	C.5 FS-2
21	C.7	Sign-off Software	10	C.6
22	C.8	Conduct Data Migration	60	C.6 SS+40
23	C.9	Sign-off Implementation	10	C.8
24	C.10	Go Live	5	C.9
25	D	Monitoring & Control		
26	D.1	Set up Quality Review Process	3	B.5
27	D.2	Perform Project Internal Audit	15	D.1
28	D.3	Track Project Performance	20	B.5,D.1
29	D.4	Perform Project External Audit	3	D.2,D.3
30	E	Closing		
31	E.1	Conduct Staff Training on New System	8	C.7
32	E.2	Compile Best Practices for use of New System	5	C.9
33	E.3	Compile Lessons Learnt Document	3	C.10
34	E.4	Complete Project Accounting	5	C.10,E.3 FF
35	E.5	Conduct Project Closure Meeting	1	C.10,D.4,E.1,E.2,E.3,E.4

Figure 1.22: *WBS with predecessors for all the tasks set*

Creating the project network

Now that we have identified the predecessors for every task, we can create the project network. The project network shows the relationship between each task through a picture, as shown in *figure 1.23*:

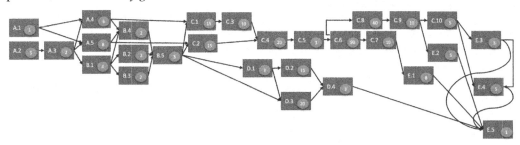

Figure 1.23: *Project network*

The diagramming method used to create the project network in *figure 1.23* is called the **Precedence Diagramming Method (PDM)**.

In the *figure 1.23*, the project starts from the tasks on the left-hand side and progresses to the tasks on the right-hand side. The project ends with task E.5.

Calculating the project duration

We can calculate the project duration once we have the project network. As our network is quite large, let's take a part of the network and demonstrate the method to calculate the project duration. We will calculate the duration graphically for this small part of our project and then use *Microsoft Excel* to calculate the project duration for our entire project.

Let's consider that the duration of the tasks is in days. It could also be in other units, like weeks, months, fortnights, years, or hours.

Let's consider a part of the project, as shown in *figure 1.24*, as our complete project and calculate the duration:

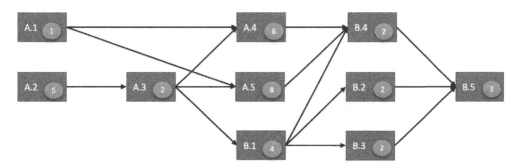

Figure 1.24: Part of the project network to consider for calculating the project duration

Conducting the forward pass

We will begin the calculation of the project duration with the tasks at the left of the project network. We notice that the tasks A.1 and A.2 do not have any predecessor, so they can start on the first day of the project. Hence, we assign the start date of the tasks A.1 and A.2 as 1, as shown in *figure 1.25*:

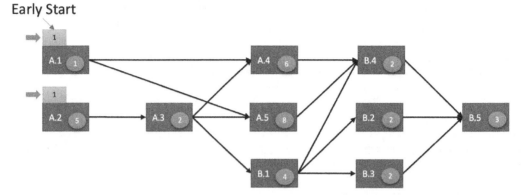

Figure 1.25: Assigning early start to tasks A.1 and A.2

The date we have assigned to tasks A.1 and A.2 is called the **Early Start (ES)** date of tasks A.1 and A.2. *Early Start is the date when a task can start at the earliest in the project.*

Once we have the ES for a task, we can compute the **Early Finish (EF)** date of the task:

$$Early\ Finish\ (EF) = Early\ Start\ (ES) + Duration - 1$$

Early Finish is the date when a task can be expected to complete at the earliest in the project.

So, we can compute the EF for tasks A.1 and A.2 as shown in *figure 1.26*:

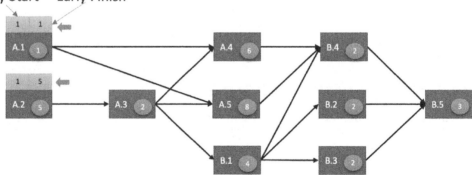

Figure 1.26: Assigning early finish to tasks A.1 and A.2

In *figure 1.26*, note that task A.3 follows A.2, and task A.3 has a finish-to-start relationship with task A.2. So, task A.3 can start only after task A.2 has been completed. Task A.2 finishes on day 5, so task A.3 can start only on day 6. So, the early start for task A.3 is 6, as shown in *figure 1.27*:

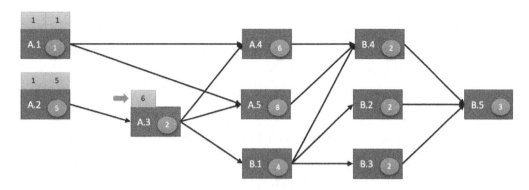

Figure 1.27: *Assigning early start to task A.3*

Now, we can calculate the early finish for task A.3 as shown in *figure 1.28*:

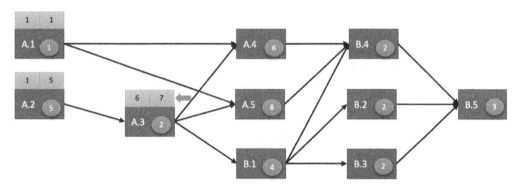

Figure 1.28: *Assigning early finish to task A.3*

Like task A.3, we note that tasks B.1, B.2, and B.3 have only one predecessor task in A.3, B.1, and B.1, respectively. Also, the relationship between tasks B.1 and A.3, B.2 and B.1, and B.3 and B.1 is finish-to-start, so we can calculate the early start and early finish for tasks B.1, B.2, and B.3, as shown in *figure 1.29*:

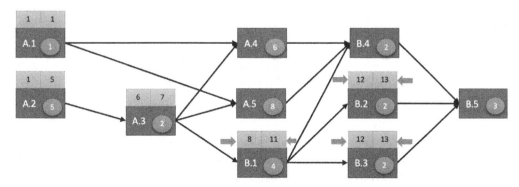

Figure 1.29: *Assigning early start and early finish to tasks B.1, B.2, and B.3*

Now, let's look at task A.4. Note that task A.4 has two predecessors in tasks A.1 and A.3. Also, task A.4 has a finish-to-start relationship with both task A.1 and task A.3. So, task A.4 cannot start before both these tasks are completed. So, the earliest task A.4 can start is one day after both tasks A.1 and A.3 are completed.

So, we can calculate early start of task A.4 as the maximum of early finish of tasks A.1 and A.3 plus 1:

ES for A.4 = maximum(EF of A.1, EF of A.3) + 1

We can compute the early finish of task A.4 once we get the early start of task A.4. So, we get the early start and early finish of task A.4, as shown in *figure 1.30*:

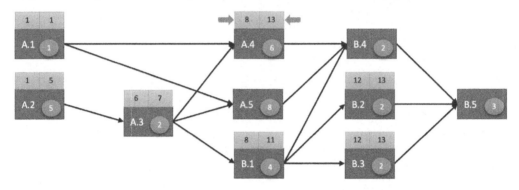

Figure 1.30: *Assigning early start and early finish to task A.4*

Similarly, we can calculate the early start and early finish of task A.5, as shown in *figure 1.31*:

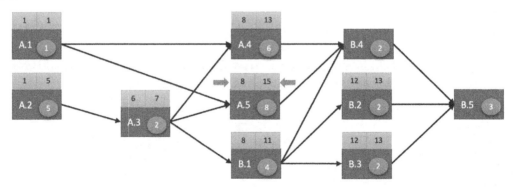

Figure 1.31: *Assigning early start and early finish to task A.5*

Next, we will find the early start and early finish for task B.4. We note that task B.4 has three predecessor tasks in A.4, A.5, and B.1, and the relationship between tasks B.4 and A.4, tasks B.4 and A.5, and tasks B.4 and B.1 is a finish-to-start relationship.

So, as with task A.4, we can compute the early start of task B.4 as the maximum of the early finish of tasks A.4, A.5, and B.1 plus 1:

ES for B.4 = maximum(EF of A.4, EF of A.5, EF of B.1) + 1

We can compute the early finish of task B.4 once we get the early start of task B.4, as shown in *figure 1.32*:

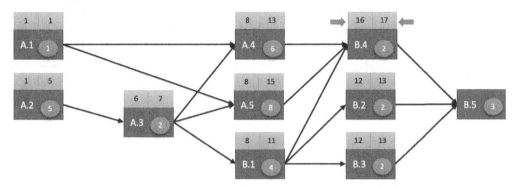

Figure 1.32: Assigning early start and early finish to task B.4

Lastly, we can compute the early start and early finish for task B.5 just like we did for task B.4:

ES for B.5 = maximum(EF of B.4, EF of B.2, EF of B.3) + 1

We can compute the early finish for task B.5 once we get the early start of task B.5, as shown in *figure 1.33*:

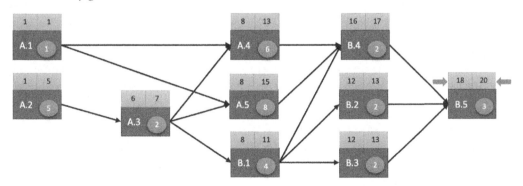

Figure 1.33: Assigning early start and early finish to task B.5

If we consider that our project is as shown in *figure 1.33*, we get that the last task in our project network (i.e., task B.5) completes on day 20 after the project starts. So, we get that the duration of this project is 20 days.

Conducting the backward pass

We could establish the duration of the project after conducting the forward pass over our project network. In the forward pass, we start with the first task and progress to the last task in the project network. In the backward pass, we start with the last task and move toward the tasks at the beginning of the project.

To start the backward pass, we consider that the last task in our project network will end on the last day of the project. As per our calculation in *figure 1.33*, the last task is B.5, and task B.5 is scheduled to end on the 20th day after the project starts. So, we will consider that task B.5 will end on the 20th day to start our backward pass. Marking task B.5 to end on the 20th day is called marking the **Late Finish (LF)** date for task B.5. *Late Finish is the maximum date on which a task can finish as per our calculations.*

We will mark the late finish date for task B.5, as shown in *figure 1.34*:

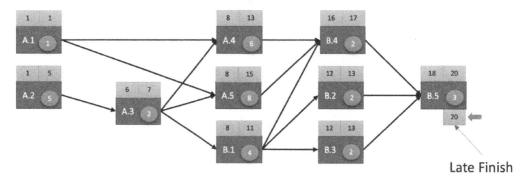

Figure 1.34: *Assigning late finish to task B.5*

Once we have the **Late Finish (LF)** date for a task, we can calculate the date when that task should start to be completed on the late finish date. This date is called the **Late Start (LS)** date. *Late Start date is the maximum date on which a task can start in the project network.*

We can calculate LS as LF minus duration for the task plus 1:

$$Late\ Start\ (LS) = Late\ Finish\ (LF) - Duration + 1$$

So, we can calculate the late start for task B.5, as shown in *figure 1.35*:

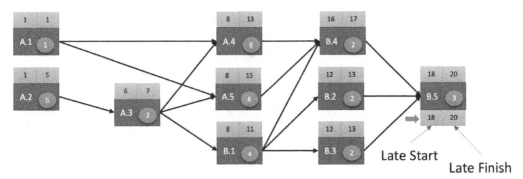

Figure 1.35: Assigning late start to task B.5

Once we have the late start for task B.5, we can calculate the late finish for tasks B.2, B.3, and B.4. This is because all these tasks finish only before task B.5 starts. Tasks B.2, B.3, and B.4 have only one successor task in task B.5. So, these tasks should end one day before the start of task B.5. In our case, the late finish for tasks B.2, B.3 and B.4 should be (18 − 1) or the 17th day after the project starts.

Refer to *figure 1.36*, where the late finish for tasks B.2, B.3, and B.4 has been marked:

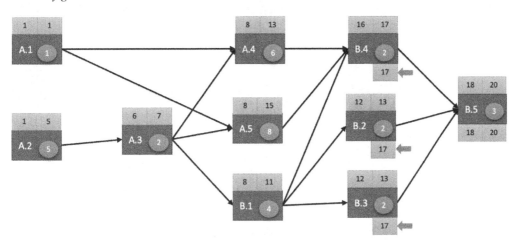

Figure 1.36: Assigning late finish to tasks B.2, B.3, and B.4

Now, we can calculate the late start for tasks B.2, B.3, and B.4, as shown in *figure 1.37*:

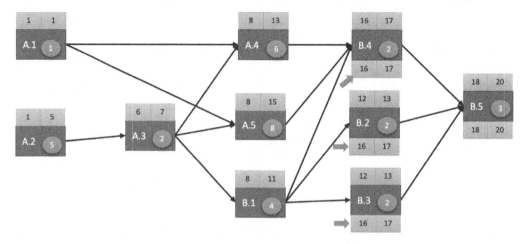

Figure 1.37: *Assigning late start to tasks B.2, B.3, and B.4*

Tasks A.4 and A.5 have one successor task in task B.4. So, we can compute the late finish and late start for tasks A.4 and A.5, as shown in *figure 1.38*:

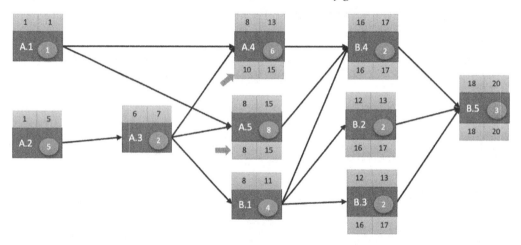

Figure 1.38: *Assigning late finish and late start to tasks A.4 and A.5*

Next, take a look at task B.4. There are 3 tasks, namely task B.2, B.3, and B.4, which are the successors of task B.1. So, task B.1 must finish before tasks B.2, B.3 and B.4 can start. So, B.1 must end before the minimum of the late start dates of tasks B.2, B.3, and B.4. We can compute the late finish date of task B.1 as follows:

Late Finish date of task B.1 = minimum(Late Start date of tasks B.2, B.3, B.4) − 1

Once we get the late finish date of task B.1, we can compute the late start date of task B.1, as shown in *figure 1.39*:

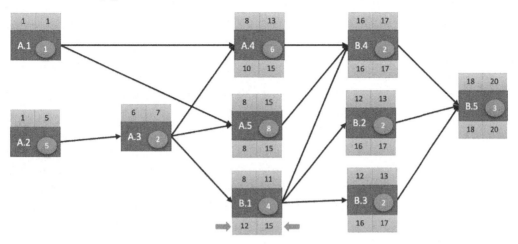

Figure 1.39: *Assigning late finish and late start to task B.1*

Now consider task A.3. Task A.3 has three successor tasks in tasks A.4, A.5, and B.1. So, we can calculate the late finish date of task A.3 as follows:

Late Finish of task A.3= minimum(Late Start of tasks A.4, A.5, B.1) – 1

Once we get the late finish of task A.3, we can compute the late start of task A.3, as shown in *figure 1.40*:

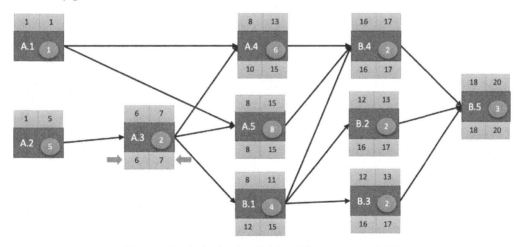

Figure 1.40: *Assigning late finish and late start to task A.3*

Now consider task A.1. Task A.1 has two successor tasks in tasks A.4 and A.5, so we can calculate the late finish of task A.1 as follows:

Late Finish of task A.1 = minimum (Late Start of tasks A.4, A.5) − 1

Once we get the late finish of task A.1, we can compute the late start of task A.1, as shown in *figure 1.41*:

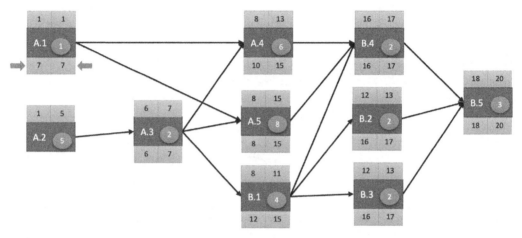

Figure 1.41: *Assigning late finish date and late start date to task A.1*

That leaves us with task A.2. Task A.2 has only one successor task in task A.3, so we can compute the late finish of task A.2 as late start of task A.3 minus 1. Then, we can compute the late start of task A.2, as shown in *figure 1.42*:

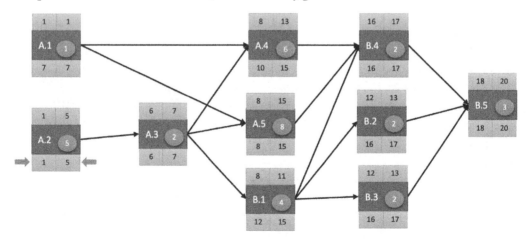

Figure 1.42: *Assigning late finish date and late start date to task A.2*

With this, we have completed the backward pass of our project network. So, we have the early start, early finish, late start, and late finish of all the tasks.

Calculating the Slack for each task

Slack is the maximum time available by which the task can be delayed without impacting the total project duration. Slack is the difference between the late start and the early start of a task, or it is the difference between the late finish and early finish of a task.

$$Slack = LF - EF = LS - ES$$

Slack is also called **Float**.

For example, for task B.1, LF is 15 and EF is 11. So, slack for task B.1 is (15-11 =) 4 days. Note that LS for task B.1 is 12 and ES for task B.1 is 8, so slack comes to (12-8 =) 4 days.

The overall project duration will not change if a task has a slack of 5 days and it is delayed by up to 5 days. Having tasks with slack reduces the risk in the project schedule. If a project schedule has few tasks with slack and further, if the amount of slack is small, the project schedule can be risky as delays in any task can delay the project.

In *figure 1.43*, we have calculated the slack for all the tasks in our project network. The slack figure is provided in a red color square in each task:

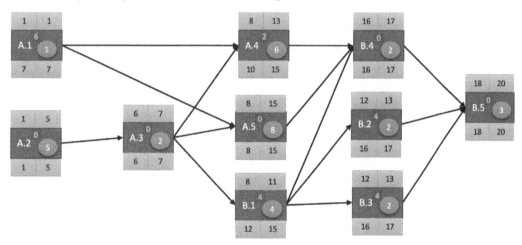

Figure 1.43: Project network showing the slack for each task

Note that the project network has tasks where the slack is zero. When the slack for a task is zero, it implies that the task cannot be delayed. The project duration will increase if tasks with zero slack are delayed.

Determining the critical path of the project

Critical Path is the longest path in the project network in terms of duration. Tasks on the critical path of a project network have zero slack, so the project will get delayed if any task on the critical path is delayed.

A project manager's major task is to manage the critical path. A project has a good chance of completion on schedule if the project manager can ensure that the critical path is not altered and the tasks on the critical path are well managed.

If tasks on the critical path get delayed, the critical path of the project may change. Also, a project network can have more than one critical path. Having more than one critical path is a sure sign that the project is risky because having more than one critical path means the project has more tasks with zero slack. Having more tasks with zero slack means a greater number of tasks in the project cannot be delayed for completing the project on time.

Start with the last task in the project network to determine the critical path from a project network. From the last task, trace the path in the project network through the tasks that have zero slack. *Figure 1.44* shows the critical path for our project:

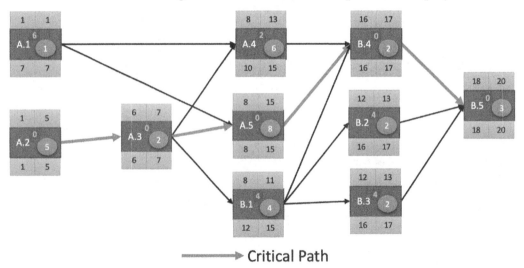

Figure 1.44: *Project network showing the critical path*

Section - II
Excel
Implementation

Let us put the theory we discussed in section 1 into an implementation using Microsoft Excel.

Calculating ES, EF, LS, LF using Microsoft Excel

Let's see how we can calculate the forward pass and backward pass using *Microsoft Excel*. First, add five columns named ES (for early start), EF (for early finish), LS (for late start), LF (for late finish), and Slack in the *Microsoft Excel* sheet, as shown in *figure 1.45*:

	A	B	C	D	E	F	G	H	I
1	Task ID	Task Description	Duration	Predecessor	ES	EF	LS	LF	Slack
2	A	Initiation							
3	A.1	Conduct Kick-off Meeting	1						
4	A.2	Create Project Charter	5						
5	A.3	Sign-off Project Charter	2	A.2					
6	A.4	Identify Hardware	6	A.1,A.3					
7	A.5	Identify Software	8	A.1,A.3					
8	B	Planning							
9	B.1	Create Project Plan	4	A.3					
10	B.2	Create Project Schedule	2	B.1					
11	B.3	Identify Team	2	B.1					
12	B.4	Allocate Budget	2	B.1,A.4,A.5					
13	B.5	Sign-off Project Plan	3	B.2,B.3,B.4					
14	C	Execution							
15	C.1	Purchase Hardware	15	A.4,B.5					
16	C.2	Purchase Software	15	A.5,B.5					
17	C.3	Install Hardware	10	C.1					
18	C.4	Create Prototype	20	C.2,C.3 FS+2					
19	C.5	Sign-off Prototype	3	C.4					
20	C.6	Customise Software	90	C.5 FS-2					
21	C.7	Sign-off Software	10	C.6					
22	C.8	Conduct Data Migration	60	C.6 SS+40					
23	C.9	Sign-off Implementation	10	C.8					
24	C.10	Go Live	5	C.9					
25	D	Monitoring & Control							
26	D.1	Set up Quality Review Process	3	B.5					
27	D.2	Perform Project Internal Audit	15	D.1					
28	D.3	Track Project Performance	20	B.5,D.1					
29	D.4	Perform Project External Audit	3	D.2,D.3					
30	E	Closing							
31	E.1	Conduct Staff Training on New System	8	C.7					
32	E.2	Compile Best Practices for use of New System	5	C.9					
33	E.3	Compile Lessons Learnt Document	3	C.10					
34	E.4	Complete Project Accounting	5	C.10,E.3 FF					
35	E.5	Conduct Project Closure Meeting	1	C.10,D.4,E.1,E.2,E.3,E.4					

Figure 1.45: *Microsoft Excel sheet with WBS after adding columns for ES, EF, LS, LF, and Slack*

Conducting the forward pass

Tasks A.1 and A.2 do not have any predecessor, so they must begin on day 1 of the project. So, we set the cells E3 and E4 as 1 to indicate that the early start of tasks A.1 and A.2 is 1. After this, we can calculate the early finish of tasks A.1 and A.2 using the formula for early finish.

Enter the following in the mentioned cells in the Microsoft Excel Sheet:

Cell	What to Enter
E3	1
E4	1
F3	=E3+C3-1
F4	=E4+C4-1

Table 1.1: Formulae to calculate ES and EF for tasks A.1 and A.2

Task A.3 has one predecessor task in task A.2, so enter the following formulae in the mentioned cells to calculate the early start and early finish for task A.3:

Cell	What to Enter
E5	F4+1
F5	E5+C5-1

Table 1.2: Formulae to calculate ES and EF for task A.3

We can see that tasks A.4 and A.5 have two predecessors each, so enter the following in the mentioned cells to calculate the early start and early finish for tasks A.4 and A.5:

Cell	What to Enter
E6	=MAX(F3,F5)+1
E7	=MAX(F3,F5)+1
F6	=E6+C6-1
F7	=E7+C7-1

Table 1.3: Formulae to calculate ES and EF for tasks A.4 and A.5

Tasks B.1, B.2, and B.3 have only one predecessor task each, so we can calculate the early starts for these tasks by adding 1 to the early finish of the predecessor tasks. Enter the following in the mentioned cells to calculate the early start and early finish for tasks B.1, B.2, and B.3:

Cell	What to Enter
E9	=F5+1
E10	=F9+1
E11	=F9+1
F9	=E9+C9-1

| F10 | =E10+C10-1 |
| F11 | =E11+C11-1 |

Table 1.4: *Formulae to calculate ES and EF for tasks B.1, B.2, and B.3*

Tasks B.4 and B.5 have three predecessor tasks each, so enter the following in the mentioned cells to calculate the early start and early finish for tasks B.4 and B.5:

Cell	What to Enter
E12	=MAX(F6,F7,F9)+1
E13	=MAX(F10,F11,F12)+1
F12	=E12+C12-1
F13	=E13+C13-1

Table 1.5: *Formulae to calculate ES and EF for tasks B.4 and B.5*

We had calculated the early start and early finish for the tasks from A.1 through B.5 graphically. Now, let's refer to our Microsoft Excel sheet with the formulae entered in the cells mentioned above and compare the calculations. The resultant Microsoft Excel sheet is displayed in *figure 1.46*:

	A	B	C	D	E	F	G	H	I
1	Task ID	Task Description	Duration	Predecessor	ES	EF	LS	LF	Slack
2	A	Initiation							
3	A.1	Conduct Kick-off Meeting	1		1	1			
4	A.2	Create Project Charter	5		1	5			
5	A.3	Sign-off Project Charter	2	A.2	6	7			
6	A.4	Identify Hardware	6	A.1,A.3	8	13			
7	A.5	Identify Software	8	A.1,A.3	8	15			
8	B	Planning							
9	B.1	Create Project Plan	4	A.3	8	11			
10	B.2	Create Project Schedule	2	B.1	12	13			
11	B.3	Identify Team	2	B.1	12	13			
12	B.4	Allocate Budget	2	B.1,A.4,A.5	16	17			
13	B.5	Sign-off Project Plan	3	B.2,B.3,B.4	18	20			
14	C	Execution							
15	C.1	Purchase Hardware	15	A.4,B.5					
16	C.2	Purchase Software	15	A.5,B.5					
17	C.3	Install Hardware	10	C.1					
18	C.4	Create Prototype	20	C.2,C.3 FS+2					
19	C.5	Sign-off Prototype	3	C.4					
20	C.6	Customise Software	90	C.5 FS-2					
21	C.7	Sign-off Software	10	C.6					
22	C.8	Conduct Data Migration	60	C.6 SS+40					
23	C.9	Sign-off Implementation	10	C.8					
24	C.10	Go Live	5	C.9					
25	D	Monitoring & Control							
26	D.1	Set up Quality Review Process	3	B.5					
27	D.2	Perform Project Internal Audit	15	D.1					
28	D.3	Track Project Performance	20	B.5,D.1					
29	D.4	Perform Project External Audit	3	D.2,D.3					
30	E	Closing							
31	E.1	Conduct Staff Training on New System	8	C.7					
32	E.2	Compile Best Practices for use of New System	5	C.9					
33	E.3	Compile Lessons Learnt Document	3	C.10					
34	E.4	Complete Project Accounting	5	C.10,E.3 FF					
35	E.5	Conduct Project Closure Meeting	1	C.10,D.4,E.1,E.2,E.3,E.4					

Figure 1.46: *Updated Microsoft Excel sheet*
after entering the formulae for calculating ES and EF for tasks A.1 through B.5

Now, let's fill the formulae for tasks C.1 through E.5.

Tasks C.1 and C.2 have two predecessor tasks each, so enter the following formulae in the mentioned cells to calculate the early start and early finish for tasks C.1 and C.2:

Cell	What to Enter
E15	=MAX(F6,F13)+1
E16	=MAX(F7,F13)+1
F15	=E15+C15-1
F16	=E16+C16-1

Table 1.6: Formulae to calculate ES and EF for tasks C.1 and C.2

Task C.3 has only predecessor task, so we can enter the following formulae in the mentioned cells:

Cell	What to Enter
E17	=F15+1
F17	=E17+C17-1

Table 1.7: Formulae to calculate ES and EF for task C.3

We have a new case while dealing with task C.4. This task starts with lag. Task C.3 has two predecessor tasks in C.2 and C.3, so we need to take the maximum of the early finish of task C.2 and early finish of task C.3 to calculate the early start for task C.4. Add 2 days—as there is a positive lag of 2 days—to the early finish of task C.3:

$$ES \text{ of task } C.4 = maximum(EF \text{ of task } C.2, EF \text{ of task } C.3 + 2) + 1$$

For task C.4, enter the following formulae in the mentioned cells:

Cell	What to Enter
E18	=MAX(F16,F17+2)+1
F18	=E18+C18-1

Table 1.8: Formulae to calculate ES and EF for task C.4

The calculation of early start and early finish for task C.5 is simple. Enter the following formulae in the mentioned cells:

Cell	What to Enter
E19	=F18+1
F19	=E19+C19-1

Table 1.9: Formulae to calculate ES and EF for task C.5

We have a new case for task C.6. Task C.6 has only one predecessor task, but it starts with a negative lag in a finish-to-start relationship. Enter the following formulae in the mentioned cells:

Cell	What to Enter
E20	=F19-2+1
F20	=E20+C20-1

Table 1.10: Formulae to calculate ES and EF for task C.6

The calculation of early start and early finish for task C.7 is simple. Enter the following formulae in the mentioned cells:

Cell	What to Enter
E21	=F20+1
F21	=E21+C21-1

Table 1.11: Formulae to calculate ES and EF for task C.7

So far, we have only dealt with a finish-to-start relationship between two tasks. Now, we have a start-to-start relationship between task C.8 and task C.6. We need to take the early start of task C.6 and assign it to task C.8 to calculate the early start for task C.8. However, task C.8 has a positive lag of 40 days, so the early start for task C.8 is equal to the early start of task C.6 + 40. Enter the following formulae in the mentioned cells:

Cell	What to Enter
E22	=E20+40
F22	=E22+C22-1

Table 1.12: Formulae to calculate ES and EF for task C.8

The calculation of early start and early finish for tasks C.9 and C.10 is simple. Enter the following formulae in the mentioned cells:

Cell	What to Enter
E23	=F22+1
E24	=F23+1
F23	=E23+C23-1
F24	=E24+C24-1

Table 1.13: Formulae to calculate ES and EF for tasks C.9 and C.10

Let's look at our spreadsheet after the calculations we have conducted so far. *Figure 1.47* shows the updated spreadsheet:

	A	B	C	D	E	F	G	H	I
1	Task ID	Task Description	Duration	Predecessor	ES	EF	LS	LF	Slack
2	A	Initiation							
3	A.1	Conduct Kick-off Meeting	1		1	1			
4	A.2	Create Project Charter	5		1	5			
5	A.3	Sign-off Project Charter	2	A.2	6	7			
6	A.4	Identify Hardware	6	A.1,A.3	8	13			
7	A.5	Identify Software	8	A.1,A.3	8	15			
8	B	Planning							
9	B.1	Create Project Plan	4	A.3	8	11			
10	B.2	Create Project Schedule	2	B.1	12	13			
11	B.3	Identify Team	2	B.1	12	13			
12	B.4	Allocate Budget	2	B.1,A.4,A.5	16	17			
13	B.5	Sign-off Project Plan	3	B.2,B.3,B.4	18	20			
14	C	Execution							
15	C.1	Purchase Hardware	15	A.4,B.5	21	35			
16	C.2	Purchase Software	15	A.5,B.5	21	35			
17	C.3	Install Hardware	10	C.1	36	45			
18	C.4	Create Prototype	20	C.2,C.3 FS+2	48	67			
19	C.5	Sign-off Prototype	3	C.4	68	70			
20	C.6	Customise Software	90	C.5 FS-2	69	158			
21	C.7	Sign-off Software	10	C.6	159	168			
22	C.8	Conduct Data Migration	60	C.6 SS+40	109	168			
23	C.9	Sign-off Implementation	10	C.8	169	178			
24	C.10	Go Live	5	C.9	179	183			
25	D	Monitoring & Control							
26	D.1	Set up Quality Review Process	3	B.5					
27	D.2	Perform Project Internal Audit	15	D.1					
28	D.3	Track Project Performance	20	B.5,D.1					
29	D.4	Perform Project External Audit	3	D.2,D.3					
30	E	Closing							
31	E.1	Conduct Staff Training on New System	8	C.7					
32	E.2	Compile Best Practices for use of New System	5	C.9					
33	E.3	Compile Lessons Learnt Document	3	C.10					
34	E.4	Complete Project Accounting	5	C.10,E.3 FF					
35	E.5	Conduct Project Closure Meeting	1	C.10,D.4,E.1,E.2,E.3,E.4					

Figure 1.47: *Updated Microsoft Excel sheet after entering the formulae for calculating ES and EF for tasks A.1 through C.10*

Tasks D.1, D.2, D.3 and D.4 are audit tasks and will occur across the complete project lifetime. The duration mentioned for these tasks is the total amount of time that will be consumed in performing these tasks. However, we cannot compute the start date and end date for these tasks as they will be scheduled as per the quality team's judgment and convenience. So, we will not compute the early start and early end for the tasks D.1, D.2, D.3, and D.4.

Calculating ES and EF for tasks E.1, E.2, and E.3 should be simple, so enter the following formulae in the mentioned cells:

Cell	What to Enter
E31	=F21+1
E32	=F23+1
E33	=F24+1
F31	=E31+C31-1
F32	=E32+C32-1
F33	=E33+C33-1

Table 1.14: *Formulae to calculate ES and EF for tasks E.1, E.2, and E.3*

Now, we have come to a new type of relationship in our network where we have a finish-to-finish relationship between tasks E.4 and E.3. Task E.4 also has a finish-to-start relationship with task C.10.

Before we discuss the calculations for task E.4, let's look at our spreadsheet (refer to *figure 1.48*):

	A	B	C	D	E	F	G	H	I
1	Task ID	Task Description	Duration	Predecessor	ES	EF	LS	LF	Slack
2	A	Initiation							
3	A.1	Conduct Kick-off Meeting	1		1	1			
4	A.2	Create Project Charter	5		1	5			
5	A.3	Sign-off Project Charter	2	A.2	6	7			
6	A.4	Identify Hardware	6	A.1,A.3	8	13			
7	A.5	Identify Software	8	A.1,A.3	8	15			
8	B	Planning							
9	B.1	Create Project Plan	4	A.3	8	11			
10	B.2	Create Project Schedule	2	B.1	12	13			
11	B.3	Identify Team	2	B.1	12	13			
12	B.4	Allocate Budget	2	B.1,A.4,A.5	16	17			
13	B.5	Sign-off Project Plan	3	B.2,B.3,B.4	18	20			
14	C	Execution							
15	C.1	Purchase Hardware	15	A.4,B.5	21	35			
16	C.2	Purchase Software	15	A.5,B.5	21	35			
17	C.3	Install Hardware	10	C.1	36	45			
18	C.4	Create Prototype	20	C.2,C.3 FS+2	48	67			
19	C.5	Sign-off Prototype	3	C.4	68	70			
20	C.6	Customise Software	90	C.5 FS-2	69	158			
21	C.7	Sign-off Software	10	C.6	159	168			
22	C.8	Conduct Data Migration	60	C.6 SS+40	109	168			
23	C.9	Sign-off Implementation	10	C.8	169	178			
24	C.10	Go Live	5	C.9	179	183			
25	D	Monitoring & Control							
26	D.1	Set up Quality Review Process	3	B.5					
27	D.2	Perform Project Internal Audit	15	D.1					
28	D.3	Track Project Performance	20	B.5,D.1					
29	D.4	Perform Project External Audit	3	D.2,D.3					
30	E	Closing							
31	E.1	Conduct Staff Training on New System	8	C.7	169	176			
32	E.2	Compile Best Practices for use of New System	5	C.9	179	183			
33	E.3	Compile Lessons Learnt Document	3	C.10	184	186			
34	E.4	Complete Project Accounting	5	C.10,E.3 FF					
35	E.5	Conduct Project Closure Meeting	1	C.10,D.4,E.1,E.2,E.3,E.4					

Figure 1.48: *Updated Microsoft Excel sheet after entering the formulae to calculate ES and EF for tasks A.1 through E.3*

Let's first consider that task E.4 only has a relationship with task E.3 and the relationship is finish-to-finish. We can calculate the early start for task E.4 as follows:

ES for task E.4 = EF for task E.3 – Duration for task E.4 + 1

However, task E.4 also has a finish-to-start relationship with task C.10, so enter the following formulae in the mentioned cells to calculate the early start and early finish for task E.4:

Cell	What to Enter
E34	=MAX(F24,F33-C34+1)+1
F34	=E34+C34-1

Table 1.15: *Formulae to calculate ES and EF for task E.4*

Enter the following formulae in the mentioned cells to calculate the early start and early finish for task E.5:

Cell	What to Enter
E35	=MAX(F24,F31,F32,F33,F34)+1
F35	=E35+C35-1

Table 1.16: *Formulae to calculate ES and EF for task E.5*

At the end of the forward pass, our spreadsheet looks as shown in *figure 1.49*:

	A	B	C	D	E	F	G	H	I
1	Task ID	Task Description	Duration	Predecessor	ES	EF	LS	LF	Slack
2	A	Initiation							
3	A.1	Conduct Kick-off Meeting	1		1	1			
4	A.2	Create Project Charter	5		1	5			
5	A.3	Sign-off Project Charter	2	A.2	6	7			
6	A.4	Identify Hardware	6	A.1,A.3	8	13			
7	A.5	Identify Software	8	A.1,A.3	8	15			
8	B	Planning							
9	B.1	Create Project Plan	4	A.3	8	11			
10	B.2	Create Project Schedule	2	B.1	12	13			
11	B.3	Identify Team	2	B.1	12	13			
12	B.4	Allocate Budget	2	B.1,A.4,A.5	16	17			
13	B.5	Sign-off Project Plan	3	B.2,B.3,B.4	18	20			
14	C	Execution							
15	C.1	Purchase Hardware	15	A.4,B.5	21	35			
16	C.2	Purchase Software	15	A.5,B.5	21	35			
17	C.3	Install Hardware	10	C.1	36	45			
18	C.4	Create Prototype	20	C.2,C.3 FS+2	48	67			
19	C.5	Sign-off Prototype	3	C.4	68	70			
20	C.6	Customise Software	90	C.5 FS-2	69	158			
21	C.7	Sign-off Software	10	C.6	159	168			
22	C.8	Conduct Data Migration	60	C.6 SS+40	109	168			
23	C.9	Sign-off Implementation	10	C.8	169	178			
24	C.10	Go Live	5	C.9	179	183			
25	D	Monitoring & Control							
26	D.1	Set up Quality Review Process	3	B.5					
27	D.2	Perform Project Internal Audit	15	D.1					
28	D.3	Track Project Performance	20	B.5,D.1					
29	D.4	Perform Project External Audit	3	D.2,D.3					
30	E	Closing							
31	E.1	Conduct Staff Training on New System	8	C.7	169	176			
32	E.2	Compile Best Practices for use of New System	5	C.9	179	183			
33	E.3	Compile Lessons Learnt Document	3	C.10	184	186			
34	E.4	Complete Project Accounting	5	C.10,E.3 FF	184	188			
35	E.5	Conduct Project Closure Meeting	1	C.10,D.4,E.1,E.2,E.3,E.4	189	189			

Figure 1.49: *Updated Microsoft Excel sheet at the end of the forward pass*

So, we get that the project duration is 189 days. We have assumed all durations in days, but we could have considered the unit of duration to be anything, like weeks or months.

Calculating the Slack for each task

We can calculate the slack for each task after we have the result of the forward pass and backward pass so that we can determine the critical path. We know that the slack is the difference between the early start and late start or the difference between early finish and late finish.

We can calculate the slack for task A.1 using the following formula:

Cell	What to Enter
I3	=H3-F3

Table 1.17: Formula for calculating slack

The formula in cell I3 can be copied to the cell for the slack of the rest of the tasks to obtain the slack for all the tasks. The result is shown in *figure 1.50*:

	A	B	C	D	E	F	G	H	I
1	Task ID	Task Description	Duration	Predecessor	ES	EF	LS	LF	Slack
2	A	Initiation							
3	A.1	Conduct Kick-off Meeting	1		1	1			
4	A.2	Create Project Charter	5		1	5			
5	A.3	Sign-off Project Charter	2	A.2	6	7			
6	A.4	Identify Hardware	6	A.1,A.3	8	13			
7	A.5	Identify Software	8	A.1,A.3	8	15			
8	B	Planning							
9	B.1	Create Project Plan	4	A.3	8	11			
10	B.2	Create Project Schedule	2	B.1	12	13			
11	B.3	Identify Team	2	B.1	12	13			
12	B.4	Allocate Budget	2	B.1,A.4,A.5	16	17			
13	B.5	Sign-off Project Plan	3	B.2,B.3,B.4	18	20			
14	C	Execution							
15	C.1	Purchase Hardware	15	A.4,B.5	21	35			
16	C.2	Purchase Software	15	A.5,B.5	21	35			
17	C.3	Install Hardware	10	C.1	36	45			
18	C.4	Create Prototype	20	C.2,C.3 FS+2	48	67			
19	C.5	Sign-off Prototype	3	C.4	68	70			
20	C.6	Customise Software	90	C.5 FS-2	69	158			
21	C.7	Sign-off Software	10	C.6	159	168			
22	C.8	Conduct Data Migration	60	C.6 SS+40	109	168			
23	C.9	Sign-off Implementation	10	C.8	169	178			
24	C.10	Go Live	5	C.9	179	183			
25	D	Monitoring & Control							
26	D.1	Set up Quality Review Process	3	B.5					
27	D.2	Perform Project Internal Audit	15	D.1					
28	D.3	Track Project Performance	20	B.5,D.1					
29	D.4	Perform Project External Audit	3	D.2,D.3					
30	E	Closing							
31	E.1	Conduct Staff Training on New System	8	C.7	169	176			
32	E.2	Compile Best Practices for use of New System	5	C.9	179	183			
33	E.3	Compile Lessons Learnt Document	3	C.10	184	186			
34	E.4	Complete Project Accounting	5	C.10,E.3 FF	184	188			
35	E.5	Conduct Project Closure Meeting	1	C.10,D.4,E.1,E.2,E.3,E.4	189	189	189	189	

Figure 1.50: Updated Microsoft Excel sheet at the end of conducting the forward pass and the backward pass and calculating the slack for each task

Can you determine the critical path for this project? Consider this an exercise.

Conclusion

Having set up our imaginary project, we created the WBS for our project. The WBS is essential before we can create the schedule for any project. After having knowledge of the tasks to perform, we considered how much time we would need to perform each task and then sequenced the tasks.

We discussed that for sequencing the tasks, we can have different types of relationships between two tasks. We can create the project network once we have the tasks, the duration for each task, and the sequence of the tasks. From the project network, we can calculate the project duration by performing the forward pass. Then, we conduct the backward pass to determine the slack in each task. With this information, we can find the critical path for a project.

Arriving at the critical path is essential for project management as the critical path is the longest path in the project network. The critical path needs to be managed to ensure that the project is completed on time.

In the next chapter, we will deal with the cost management aspect of a project. We will then proceed to the **Earned Value Method (EVM)**.

Points to remember

- Scope, schedule, and cost are the three pillars of any project. Managing them efficiently and effectively provides a good chance for the project to be successful.

- Formula for 3-point estimation, *Estimate = (O + 4M + P) / 6*, where O is the optimistic estimate, M is the most likely estimate, and P is the pessimistic estimate.

- Early start (ES) is the earliest point where a task can be started in a project.

- Early finish (EF) is the earliest point where a task can be completed in a project.

- Late start (LS) is the maximum point where a task should start in a project so that the project is not delayed.

- Late finish (LF) is the maximum point where a task should complete in a project so that the project is not delayed.

- *EF = ES + Duration - 1*

- *LS = LF – Duration + 1*

- *Slack = LF – EF = LS – ES*

- Critical path is the longest path in the project.

- All tasks on the critical path have zero slack.

Multiple choice questions

1. **What is the Slack of the tasks on the Critical Path?**

    a. 10

    b. 1

    c. 0

    d. Varies from one project to another

2. **Critical Path is:**

    a. the shortest path in a project network

    b. the longest path in a project network

    c. the path with average duration in a project network

    d. None of the above

3. **Early Start indicates:**

    a. the earliest a task can begin

    b. the maximum time of a task

    c. the minimum time of a task

    d. None of the above

4. **The formula to estimate the task duration as per Beta Distribution is:**

    a. $(O + M + P) / 3$

    b. $(O + 4M + P) / 6$

    c. $(O + M + P) / 6$

    d. $(O + 4M + P) / 3$

5. **The method for using optimistic, pessimistic, and the most probable duration for estimating task duration is called:**

    a. Parametric estimation method

    b. Delphi estimation method

    c. OPM estimation method

    d. 3-point estimation method

Answers

1. c
2. b
3. a
4. b
5. d

Questions

1. Draw the project network for the WBS shown in *figure 1.51*. What is the duration of the project?

Activity	Duration	Predecessor
A	9	
B	1	
C	2	A
D	1	B
E	1	B
F	2	C
G	1	D
H	1	E
M	1	F,G
J	2	F,H
K	1	M,J
L	1	K

Figure 1.51: WBS for Question 1

2. Calculate the ES, EF, LS, and LF for the WBS shown in the *figure 1.52*. What is the duration of the project?

Task	Duration	Predecessor
a	5	
b	3	a
c	5	b
d	7	a
e	1.5	c,d
f	8	d
g	3	e,f
h	3	e
i	4	g,h
j	2	i
k	2	j

Figure 1.52: WBS for Question 2

Key terms

- **WBS**: Work Breakdown Structure
- **PDM**: Precedence Diagramming Method
- **ES**: Early Start
- **EF**: Early Finish
- **LS**: Late Start
- **LF**: Late Finish

CHAPTER 2
Earned Value Method

In the previous chapter, we discussed the schedule component of project planning. Our goal was to estimate the duration of the project and ensure that the project schedule posed the least amount of risk to the project team. In this chapter, we will discuss the cost component of project planning.

We will start with a discussion of the cost-based pricing to understand how projects are priced. Based on what price a project is sold at, the project manager gets funds for executing the project. So, if a project is not priced right, it can cause severe concerns for the project manager.

Once the project is won at a desirable price, the project manager is allocated funds to execute the project. As the project progresses, it is important to constantly keep a tab on how much money is being spent against what was budgeted. For this monitoring, we will discuss the *earned value method* of project tracking.

The earned value method is a mathematical model that makes it easy to assess a project at any point of time during its execution. Using the earned value method, we can make decisions like whether the project is ahead of or behind schedule, whether it is within budget or has overshot the budget, and such.

In this chapter, Indian rupees is used as the currency for all discussions. You can replace Indian rupees with any other currency according to your project costs. The concepts and calculations will remain the same.

Structure

We will discuss the following topics in this chapter:

- Cost-based pricing
  - o Components of the cost
  - o Hardware cost
  - o Software cost
  - o Manpower cost
  - o Calculating bid price
- Budget At Completion (BAC)
- Creating the Gantt chart for the project
- Blended rate
- Planned Value (PV)
- Earned Value (EV)
- Actual Cost (AC)
- Schedule Variance (SV)
- Cost Variance (CV)
- Schedule Performance Index (SPI)
- Cost Performance Index (CPI)
- Estimate At Completion (EAC)
- Estimate To Complete (ETC)
- Variance At Completion (VAC)
- To Complete Performance Index (TCPI)
- Percent Complete Index - Budget Cost (PCI-B)
- Percent Complete Index - Actual Cost (PCI-C)

Objectives

After studying this unit, you will be able to understand the concept of cost-based pricing and compute the bid price for a project. You will also understand the components of the **Earned Value Method** (**EVM**) and learn how to assess a project using EVM.

Cost-based pricing

In the previous chapter, we created a plan for the execution of the project for implementing a new library management system. The situation was that we had the project and needed to move ahead to complete the same. We will take a step back now. We will consider ourselves at the stage where we are bidding to get a project.

To bid for a project, we would have received the requirement for the project from the organization needing the project to be executed. The requirement for accepting a bid from a vendor is normally requested by issuing a **Request For Proposal (RFP)**. The RFP details the technical requirements, the required implementation timelines, terms and conditions of the engagement, minimum qualification benchmarks of the vendors, details of the bid bond amount to be deposited, the required documents and certificates to be attached, and so on. RFPs may be open or closed. Open RFPs are available to all vendors wishing to pursue the opportunity, while closed RFPs are issued to select vendors by the incumbent company.

The response to RFPs requires the detailed technical solution proposed, the details of the project plan, and the details of the proposed price, along with other details as required by the incumbent company. We will focus on only one component of the response to the RFPs—the price component. We will now discuss how we can arrive at a price that we will propose in response to an RFP.

We will identify all the components of the involved costs to determine the bid price. We will determine the sale price from these costs. This mechanism of pricing is known as **cost-based pricing**.

Components of the cost

The first step to arrive at the price to quote is to identify the components of the cost. Let's say that we identify the following cost components in the project for new library management system implementation:

- Hardware cost
- Software cost
- Manpower cost

There are other costs in the project as well, like travel cost, onsite visit cost, customer entertainment costs, and such. However, we will not consider them for our discussion.

Hardware cost

With regard to hardware cost, a software implementer will generally procure the hardware from a hardware manufacturer's dealer or an **Original Equipment**

Manufacturer (OEM) of the brand. It is very rare that the manufacturers of the hardware also sell the application software. Let's assume, for our discussion, that the software implementer is a system integrator and does not manufacture hardware. So, this company must procure the hardware and supply it to the customer.

Now, system integrators have two basic strategies. There are many system integrators who supply the hardware to customers at the same price as they would have spent to procure the hardware. This strategy is used for two reasons. The first and the main reason is that the overall bid price is low when this strategy this used. Bidding at the lowest possible price enhances the chances of winning the bid.

The second reason is that the system integrators mainly want to make profits through the services they provide. The system integrators earn reasonably from the development and deployment of the required system. They maximize their profits once the system goes into the maintenance and enhancement phase through change requests.

There are many large system integrators, like IBM and Oracle, who also supply their own hardware as part of the contract. However, even companies like IBM have exited from this strategy and only focus on supplying the services.

The second strategy used by system integrators is to mark up the price at which they procure the hardware from the hardware supplier. This strategy is applied when the system integrator is confident that they can win the bid even after this increase in the bid price or when the cost involved in procuring the hardware is not justified to be waived off by the system integrator. It is justified to charge this markup price as the system integrators have expenses even if they merely procure the hardware and supply the same to the customers. We can appreciate that at the very minimum, the administrative staff of the system integrator puts in effort when such a deal is done. Further, the system integrator may have a process for inspecting the equipment before supplying it to the customer. Such activities will need the system integrator to use skilled technicians.

For our discussion, let's assume that the hardware is to be procured at Rs.20,00,000 (Rupees twenty lakhs only) and supplied to the customer at Rs.25,00,000 (Rupees twenty-five lakhs only).

When a company buys any hardware, it almost always also procures maintenance services for the hardware. Now, the maintenance service is provided by the manufacturer or one of its partners in most cases. The partners are generally regional companies with proximity to the customer's installation.

The provider of the maintenance services will have many options, which will include different levels of services. We will not get into the details.

For our discussion, let's say that the annual maintenance contract is procured at Rs.4,00,000 (Rupees four lakhs only) and supplied to the customer at Rs.5,00,000

(Rupees five lakhs only). Let's also assume that the maintenance contract proposed is for a period of 3 years.

So, let's include the following in the bid:

Hardware cost = Rs.25,00,000.00

Annual Maintenance Cost (AMC) for hardware = Rs.5,00,000.00

*AMC of hardware for 3 years = Rs.5,00,000 * 3 = Rs.15,00,000.00*

Profit from hardware supply = Rs.5,00,000.00

Profit from annual maintenance contract = Rs.3,00,000.00

Item	Year 0	Year 1	Year 2	Year 3	TOTAL
Hardware Cost	₹25,00,000.00	₹0.00	₹0.00	₹0.00	₹25,00,000.00
AMC	₹0.00	₹5,00,000.00	₹5,00,000.00	₹5,00,000.00	₹15,00,000.00
TOTAL	₹25,00,000.00	₹5,00,000.00	₹5,00,000.00	₹5,00,000.00	₹40,00,000.00

Figure 2.1: Breakdown of hardware pricing

Any hardware vendor will provide a period of warranty. AMC can start only after the end of the warranty period. We have considered that the warranty period is 1 year, so the AMC starts a year after the purchase of the hardware.

Software cost

There are a few possibilities with regard to software supply. The first possibility is that vendors have their own solution to be provided as part of the bid. In this case, the vendor will have a price at which they would like to sell the software as part of the bid. The price attached in the bid is generally decided based on the criticality of the opportunity. If the customer is strategically important, then the vendor may want to attach a lower price for the software and gather mileage from this contract to be able to make more sales of the software. At the very least, the software manufacturer would like to recover the cost of developing the software. In most cases, the vendor will have a view for how many sales of the software they will be able to make in a defined period. They will then set the price of the software such that the cost is recovered from all the sales, and the desired profit is achieved.

For example, let's say that the software manufacturer has spent Rs.40,00,000 (Rupees forty lakhs only) in getting the software developed. And the company feels that they can make 10 sales in 1 year. Further, they desire to make 50% profit in the first year. In this case, the price at which the company would like to sell the software can be calculated as follows:

Cost of developing the software = Rs.40,00,000.00

Planned development cost recovery period = 1 year

Number of sales targeted in year 1 = 10

Cost per sales = Rs.40,00,000.00 / 10 = Rs.4,00,000.00

Desired Profit = 50%

Profit per sale = 50% * Rs.4,00,000.00 = Rs.2,00,000.00

So, sale price = Rs.4,00,000.00 + Rs.2,00,000.00 = Rs.6,00,000.00

Apart from the software procurement cost, the vendors generally will charge a license fee for using the software. The license cost is the means for the vendor to have recurring earnings from the customer. Vendors use several strategies to charge license fees. For example, some vendors charge fees based on the number of users using the software, while some charge license fees based on the number of cores used in the machine on which the software is deployed.

Let's consider some concrete cases of license fees. A vendor supplying software to a telecom company for billing the customers would base the license fees on the number of the telecom company's subscribers. Oracle charges license fees for its database management system based on the number of cores. A vendor supplying software to a call center company would base the license on the number of agents using the software.

Even if the vendor possesses the required software, in most cases the software will not meet all the requirements as stated in the RFP. The software will need to be customized to meet these requirements. We will consider this cost of customization in the labor costs.

Now, let's consider another possibility for software supply for a bid. There are cases wherein the system integrator provides the software from a software vendor as part of the bid. In this case, the system integrator procures the software from the software vendor and supplies it to the customer. This is like the parallel case we discussed with regard to hardware supply. Here, the system integrator may supply the software at the cost it is procured from the software manufacturer, or it may add a markup fee. In this case as well, the system integrator generally retains the task of customizing the software.

There is yet another possibility that may not be so appropriate to our project for new library management system implementation. It is that the system integrator may get the software developed by a software development company. In this case, the software development company will charge a certain fee, and the system integrator will add their own expenses on top of that to arrive at the sale price.

For our discussion, let's consider that the following is included in the bid:

Price of the software = Rs.20,00,000.00

Annual software license fee per year = Rs.4,00,000.00

Software license fee for 3 years = Rs.4,00,000.00 * 3 = Rs.12,00,000.00

Annual maintenance cost (AMC) for the software = Rs.5,00,000.00

AMC for the software for 3 years = Rs.15,00,000.00

Item	Year 0	Year 1	Year 2	Year 3	TOTAL
Software Cost	₹20,00,000.00	₹0.00	₹0.00	₹0.00	₹20,00,000.00
License Cost	₹0.00	₹4,00,000.00	₹4,00,000.00	₹4,00,000.00	₹12,00,000.00
AMC	₹0.00	₹5,00,000.00	₹5,00,000.00	₹5,00,000.00	₹15,00,000.00
TOTAL	₹20,00,000.00	₹9,00,000.00	₹9,00,000.00	₹9,00,000.00	₹47,00,000.00

Figure 2.2: Breakdown of software pricing

Manpower cost

With respect to this book, this is the main section of our interest regarding our discussion on bid pricing. In the previous chapter, we established an execution plan based on our understanding of the project's requirements and our estimations. However, RFPs usually specify the time in which the customer needs the project to be completed. Additionally, there are penalty clauses specified for delays in project delivery.

In our case, let's assume that the RFP states that the project must be delivered in 6 months. Under this constraint, we will try to establish how many resources we will need to complete the project. In general, the estimate for the activities needed in the project, the number of resources required to execute those activities, and the amount of time required for the activities is calculated by the pre-sales team. However, in almost all the cases, the pre-sales team consults the project team during this exercise. What this implies is that experts in the organization who may ultimately be assigned to execute the project are consulted. We must note that the project execution team is not formed till the order is received from the customer.

So, we must list the high-level tasks in the project. Let's revisit our WBS created in the previous chapter. It is shown in *figure 2.3*:

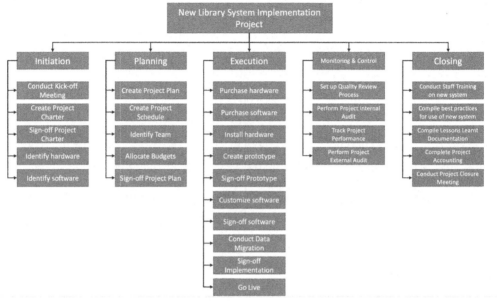

Figure 2.3: WBS for New Library Management System Implementation Project

During the bid stage, we would try to create the WBS to get a better understanding of the work involved. From this WBS, we can extract the following tasks to be done in this project:

Task ID	Task Description
A	Purchase Hardware
B	Purchase Software
A	Install Hardware
B	Create Prototype & Install Software
C	Customise Software
D	Migrate Data
E	Deploy Solution
F	Project Management Activities
G	Quality Assurance Activities

Figure 2.4: Task list for the project

Once we establish the task list, we will estimate the number of resources required for conducting the tasks within the constraints of the delivery timeline as expected by the customer. Let's say that our estimate is as shown in *figure 2.5*:

Task ID	Task Description	Number of Resources	Number of Calendar Days	Effort (in Man Days)
A	Purchase Hardware	4	5	20
B	Purchase Software	4	5	20
C	Install Hardware	2	15	30
D	Create Prototype & Install Software	3	25	75
E	Customise Software	5	60	300
F	Migrate Data	3	25	75
G	Deploy Solution	3	10	30
H	Project Management Activities	3	50	150
I	Quality Assurance Activities	3	30	90
			225	790

Figure 2.5: Effort estimates for the project

We will calculate the effort as the product of the number of resources and the number of calendar days.

*Effort = Number of Resources * Duration (Number of days required)*

Figure 2.5 provides an estimate of the amount of time required to complete the project. It seems like the project will take 225 calendar days, but we must remove the number of calendar days allocated to tasks F and G. This is because these tasks are listed as the efforts must be factored in pricing. However, these tasks will run in parallel to the other tasks throughout the project.

We need to create the project network to get a reasonable estimate of the time required. We need to plan the task precedence before we can create the project network. Let's say that we plan the task precedence as shown in *figure 2.6*:

Task ID	Task Description	Number of Resources	Number of Calendar Days	Effort (in Man Days)	Predecessor
A	Purchase Hardware	4	5	20	
B	Purchase Software	4	5	20	
C	Install Hardware	2	15	30	A
D	Create Prototype & Install Software	3	25	75	B,C
E	Customise Software	5	60	300	D
F	Migrate Data	3	25	75	D,E
G	Deploy Solution	3	10	30	F
H	Project Management Activities	3	50	150	
I	Quality Assurance Activities	3	30	90	
			225	790	

Figure 2.6: Project plan with predecessors set

Now, we can create the project network, as shown in *figure 2.7*:

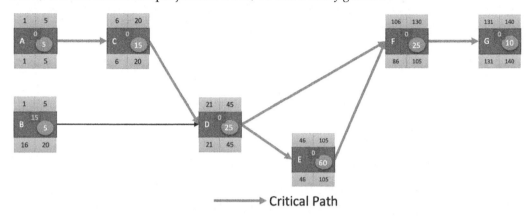

Figure 2.7: Project network

From the project network, we can see that the project can be completed in 140 days. We need to note that this does not include weekends, so we have a reasonable plan to complete the project in 6 months (which is our constraint).

We now have the number of resources required to complete the project in the given time frame. We need the rates of the resources to calculate their cost. Every organization has a rate chart for its resources, and the rate chart is generally based on the grades of the resources. We can consider an example as shown in *figure 2.8*:

Grade	Rate/month	Rate/day
I	₹ 40,000.00	₹ 2,000.00
II	₹ 60,000.00	₹ 3,000.00
III	₹ 80,000.00	₹ 4,000.00
IV	₹ 1,00,000.00	₹ 5,000.00
V	₹ 1,50,000.00	₹ 7,500.00
VI	₹ 2,00,000.00	₹ 10,000.00

Figure 2.8: Rate chart

In our plan, we will now include the number of resources of each grade, as shown in *figure 2.9*:

Task ID	Task Description	Number of Resources	Number of Calendar Days	Effort (in Man Days)	Predecessor	GRADE wise resource required					
						I	II	III	IV	V	VI
A	Purchase Hardware	4	5	20						2	2
B	Purchase Software	4	5	20						2	2
C	Install Hardware	2	15	30	A	1				1	
D	Create Prototype & Install Software	3	25	75	B,C	1			1	1	
E	Customise Software	5	60	300	D			2		2	1
F	Migrate Data	3	25	75	D,E		1	1		1	
G	Deploy Solution	3	10	30	F	1	1			1	
H	Project Management Activities	3	50	150					1	1	1
I	Quality Assurance Activities	3	30	90					1	1	1
			225	790		3	2	5	3	10	7

Figure 2.9: Number of resources allocated for each grade

Seems like we have assigned a rather senior team for this project. If the bid of execution becomes higher than the marketing team can sell the project at, one way to reduce the cost is to assign junior resources.

Now, we can calculate the cost of the resources by multiplying the *number of resources in each grade* with the *number of days of involvement required* and the *rate of the grade*. We will get the calculations as shown in *figure 2.10*.

For example, we need two resources in grade VI and two resources in grade V for task A. The cost of grade VI resources is (2 resources * 5 days * Rs.10,000 per resource per day) = Rs.1,00,000.00. The cost of grade V resources is (2 resources * 5 days * Rs.7,500 per resource per day) = Rs.75,000.00.

Task ID	Task Description	Number of Resources	Number of Calendar Days	Effort (in Man Days)	Predecessor	GRADE wise resource required						GRADE wise cost in thousands					
						I	II	III	IV	V	VI	I	II	III	IV	V	VI
A	Purchase Hardware	4	5	20						2	2	-	-	-	-	75.00	100.00
B	Purchase Software	4	5	20						2	2	-	-	-	-	75.00	100.00
C	Install Hardware	2	15	30	A	1				1		30.00	-	-	-	112.50	-
D	Create Prototype & Install Software	3	25	75	B,C	1			1	1		50.00	-	-	125.00	187.50	-
E	Customise Software	5	60	300	D			2		2	1	-	-	480.00	-	900.00	600.00
F	Migrate Data	3	25	75	D,E		1	1		1		-	75.00	100.00	-	187.50	-
G	Deploy Solution	3	10	30	F	1	1			1		20.00	30.00	-	-	75.00	-
H	Project Management Activities	3	50	150					1	1	1	-	-	200.00	250.00	-	500.00
I	Quality Assurance Activities	3	30	90					1	1	1	-	-	120.00	150.00	-	300.00
			225	790		3	2	5	3	10	7	100.00	105.00	900.00	525.00	1,612.50	1,600.00

TOTAL COST: ₹ 48,42,500.00

Figure 2.10: Total cost of resources

The cost of every grade of resources for every task is shown in terms of thousands of rupees in *figure 2.10*. So, you need to multiply by 1,000 to arrive at the actual value for all these figures. The total cost is calculated by adding the cost of all the resources in all the grades. The total cost, as shown in *figure 2.10*, is the upfront cost.

Adding risk contingency

Every project has risks. These risks need identifying at the time of estimating the project. As an example, let's say that the following risks are identified for this project:

Risk ID	Risk Description	Impact Area	Probability of Occurrence	Severity
1	Hardware and Software delivery from the vendors may be delayed	+Schedule +Cost	Medium	Medium
2	Requirement stated by Customer in RFP may change during Project Execution	+Scope +Cost +Schedule	Low	Medium
3	Customer may want changes to the prototype	+Scope +Cost +Schedule	High	Low
4	Unexpected type of data may be found during Data Migration Phase	+Schedule +Cost	High	Low
5	Key project resource may leave the project	+Schedule	Medium	Low
6	Delay in getting sign-off for the project	+Schedule +Cost	High	Medium

Figure 2.11: Risk register

Risk register will also contain the mitigation plan and contingency plan, but we are not getting into that discussion in this book. Managing risk is an entire subject and needs a book on its own.

Figure 2.11 shows a list of risks that have been qualitatively analyzed. We have identified the risks and the areas of the project that will be affected if the risk occurs. We have assigned a value of either high, medium, or low for the probability of risk occurrence. And we have assigned a value of high, medium, or low for the severity of the impact if the risk occurs.

We will go one step further to quantify the identified risks. Quantification of risk is a huge subject, so we'll use a simple working method.

Instead of assigning a value of high, medium, or low for the probability of risk occurrence, we will assign a value between 0 and 1; with 0 being the probability that the risk will not occur and 1 being the probability that the risk will certainly occur. Also, instead of assigning a value of high, medium, or low for severity, we will assign a value between 0 and 1; with 0 being no impact and 1 being severe impact. So, let's say that we get the risk register as shown in *figure 2.12*:

Risk ID	Risk Description	Impact Area	Probability of Occurrence	Severity
1	Hardware and Software delivery from the vendors may be delayed	+Schedule +Cost	0.6	0.5
2	Requirement stated by Customer in RFP may change during Project Execution	+Scope +Cost +Schedule	0.3	0.7
3	Customer may want changes to the prototype	+Scope +Cost +Schedule	0.8	0.3
4	Unexpected type of data may be found during Data Migration Phase	+Schedule +Cost	0.9	0.2
5	Key project resource may leave the project	+Schedule	0.5	0.2
6	Delay in getting sign-off for the project	+Schedule +Cost	0.9	0.6

Figure 2.12: Risk register with quantified values for the probability of occurrence and severity

Now, we calculate a risk score for each risk as the product of probability of occurrence and severity, as shown in *figure 2.13*:

$$Risk\ Score = Probability\ of\ occurrence * Severity$$

For example, the risk score for Risk ID 1 is calculated as (0.6 * 0.5) = 0.30, where 0.6 is the probability of occurrence and 0.5 is the severity.

Risk ID	Risk Description	Impact Area	Probability of Occurrence	Severity	Risk Score
1	Hardware and Software delivery from the vendors may be delayed	+Schedule +Cost	0.6	0.5	0.30
2	Requirement stated by Customer in RFP may change during Project Execution	+Scope +Cost +Schedule	0.3	0.7	0.21
3	Customer may want changes to the prototype	+Scope +Cost +Schedule	0.8	0.3	0.24
4	Unexpected type of data may be found during Data Migration Phase	+Schedule +Cost	0.9	0.2	0.18
5	Key project resource may leave the project	+Schedule	0.5	0.2	0.10
6	Delay in getting sign-off for the project	+Schedule +Cost	0.9	0.6	0.54
				TOTAL RISK SCORE:	1.57

Figure 2.13: Risk register with risk score

Based on the total risk score, the organization could set a guideline for what percentage should be added to the cost to cover for the risks. This fund that we reserve for the project to cover for risks is called the **Risk Contingency Fund**. The risk contingency fund is used as a last resort to cover the project costs. Consider that we have the guideline as shown in *figure 2.14*:

Total Risk Score	Percentage of Cost to Add as Risk Cost
0.00-0.50	5%
0.50-1.00	10%
1.00-1.50	15%
1.50-1.75	20%
1.75-2.00	25%
>2.00	30%

Figure 2.14: Guideline for adding risk cost

According to the guideline shown in *figure 2.14*, we need to add 20% of the manpower cost as risk contingency. So, risk contingency is (Rs.48,42,500 * 20%) = Rs.9,68,500.00. The calculation is shown in *figure 2.15*:

Task ID	Task Description	Number of Resources	Number of Calendar Days	Effort (in Man Days)	Predecessor	I	II	III	IV	V	VI	I	II	III	IV	V	VI
										GRADE wise resource required					GRADE wise cost in thousands	
A	Purchase Hardware	4	5	20						2	2	-	-	-	-	75.00	100.00
B	Purchase Software	4	5	20						2	2	-	-	-	-	75.00	100.00
C	Install Hardware	2	15	30	A	1					1	30.00	-	-	-	112.50	-
D	Create Prototype & Install Software	3	25	75	B,C	1			1		1	50.00	-	-	125.00	187.50	-
E	Customise Software	5	60	300	D			2		2	1	-	-	480.00	-	900.00	600.00
F	Migrate Data	3	25	75	D,E		1	1			1	-	75.00	100.00	-	187.50	-
G	Deploy Solution	3	10	30	F	1	1				1	20.00	30.00	-	-	75.00	-
H	Project Management Activities	3	50	150				1	1		1	-	-	200.00	250.00	-	500.00
I	Quality Assurance Activities	3	30	90				1	1		1	-	-	120.00	150.00	-	300.00
		225	790			3	2	5	3	10	7	100.00	105.00	900.00	525.00	1,612.50	1,600.00

A

TOTAL COST: ₹ 48,42,500.00

Risk Contingency Percentage: 20%

B

Risk Contingency: ₹ 9,68,500.00

Figure 2.15: Risk cost calculated

Adding management overhead

Every organization has costs that need to be recovered from the part of the business that earns for the organization. For example, every organization needs a finance department, human resources department, marketing department, public relations department, and such. Now, these departments are cost centers for the organization as the organization needs to spend money to keep these departments, and these departments do not produce any revenue. So, the cost of maintaining these departments needs to be recovered from the projects.

Similarly, an organization has many roles that do not directly produce any revenue. A few examples are the CXOs, directors, drivers, and cleaners. So, every organization adds a cost called the management overhead in the price for a project. Let's say that the management overhead is 15% in our case, so management contingency is (Rs.48,42,500 * 15%) = Rs.7,26,375.00. The price calculation is shown in *figure 2.16*:

Task ID	Task Description	Number of Resources	Number of Calendar Days	Effort (in Man Days)	Predecessor	GRADE wise resource required						GRADE wise cost in thousands					
						I	II	III	IV	V	VI	I	II	III	IV	V	VI
A	Purchase Hardware	4	5	20						2	2	-	-	-	-	75.00	100.00
B	Purchase Software	4	5	20						2	2	-	-	-	-	75.00	100.00
C	Install Hardware	2	15	30	A	1					1	30.00	-	-	-	112.50	-
D	Create Prototype & Install Software	3	25	75	B,C	1			1	1	50.00	-	-	125.00	187.50	-
E	Customise Software	5	60	300	D			2		2	1	-	-	480.00	-	900.00	600.00
F	Migrate Data	3	25	75	D,E		1	1		1		-	75.00	100.00	-	187.50	-
G	Deploy Solution	3	10	30	F	1	1			1		20.00	30.00	-	-	75.00	-
H	Project Management Activities	3	50	150				1	1		1	-	-	200.00	250.00	-	500.00
I	Quality Assurance Activities	3	30	90				1	1		1	-	-	120.00	150.00	-	300.00
		225		790		3	2	5	3	10	7	100.00	105.00	900.00	525.00	1,612.50	1,600.00

A   **TOTAL COST: ₹ 48,42,500.00**
    Risk Contingency Percentage: 20%
B   **Risk Contingency: ₹ 9,68,500.00**
    Management Overhead %age: 15%
C   **Management Overhead: ₹ 7,26,375.00**

Figure 2.16: *Management overhead calculated*

Adding profit

Lastly, we add the profit that we desire to make from this project. Let's say that we plan for a profit of 30%. So, planned profit is (Rs.48,42,500 * 30%) = Rs.14,52,750.00. The calculation for the profit is shown in *figure 2.17*:

Task ID	Task Description	Number of Resources	Number of Calendar Days	Effort (in Man Days)	Predecessor	GRADE wise resource required						GRADE wise cost in thousands					
						I	II	III	IV	V	VI	I	II	III	IV	V	VI
A	Purchase Hardware	4	5	20						2	2	-	-	-	-	75.00	100.00
B	Purchase Software	4	5	20						2	2	-	-	-	-	75.00	100.00
C	Install Hardware	2	15	30	A	1					1	30.00	-	-	-	112.50	-
D	Create Prototype & Install Software	3	25	75	B,C	1			1	1	50.00	-	-	125.00	187.50	-
E	Customise Software	5	60	300	D			2		2	1	-	-	480.00	-	900.00	600.00
F	Migrate Data	3	25	75	D,E		1	1		1		-	75.00	100.00	-	187.50	-
G	Deploy Solution	3	10	30	F	1	1			1		20.00	30.00	-	-	75.00	-
H	Project Management Activities	3	50	150				1	1		1	-	-	200.00	250.00	-	500.00
I	Quality Assurance Activities	3	30	90				1	1		1	-	-	120.00	150.00	-	300.00
		225		790		3	2	5	3	10	7	100.00	105.00	900.00	525.00	1,612.50	1,600.00

A   **TOTAL COST: ₹ 48,42,500.00**
    Risk Contingency Percentage: 20%
B   **Risk Contingency: ₹ 9,68,500.00**
    Management Overhead %age: 15%
C   **Management Overhead: ₹ 7,26,375.00**
    Profit Percentage: 30%
D   **Profit: ₹14,52,750.00**

Figure 2.17: *Profit calculated*

Calculating manpower cost

Now, the manpower cost for this project can be calculated by adding the upfront cost, risk contingency, management overhead, and profit, i.e., bid price is (Rs.48,42,500 +

Rs.9,68,500 + Rs.7,26,375 + Rs.14,52,750) = Rs.79,90,125.00. This is shown in *figure 2.18*:

Task ID	Task Description	Number of Resources	Number of Calendar Days	Effort (in Man Days)	Predecessor	GRADE wise resource required						GRADE wise cost in thousands					
						I	II	III	IV	V	VI	I	II	III	IV	V	VI
A	Purchase Hardware	4	5	20						2	2	-	-	-	-	75.00	100.00
B	Purchase Software	4	5	20						2	2	-	-	-	-	75.00	100.00
C	Install Hardware	2	15	30	A	1					1	30.00	-	-	-	112.50	-
D	Create Prototype & Install Software	3	25	75	B,C	1			1		1	50.00	-	-	125.00	187.50	-
E	Customise Software	5	60	300	D			2		2	1	-	-	480.00	-	900.00	600.00
F	Migrate Data	3	25	75	D,E		1	1			1	-	75.00	100.00	-	187.50	-
G	Deploy Solution	3	10	30	F	1	1				1	20.00	30.00	-	-	75.00	-
H	Project Management Activities	3	50	150				1	1		1	-	-	200.00	250.00	-	500.00
I	Quality Assurance Activities	3	30	90				1	1		1	-	-	120.00	150.00	-	300.00
			225	790		3	2	5	3	10	7	100.00	105.00	900.00	525.00	1,612.50	1,600.00

A **TOTAL COST:** ₹ 48,42,500.00
Risk Contingency Percentage: 20%
B **Risk Contingency:** ₹ 9,68,500.00
Management Overhead %age: 15%
C **Management Overhead:** ₹ 7,26,375.00
Profit Percentage: 30%
D **Profit:** ₹ 14,52,750.00

BID PRICE (A+B+C+D): ₹ 79,90,125.00

Figure 2.18: *Manpower cost calculated*

Calculating bid price

Now that we have determined all the components of the cost, we can calculate the bid price by adding all the component costs, as shown in *figure 2.19*:

Sl.	Item	Price	
1	Hardware	₹	25,00,000.00
2	AMC for Hardware	₹	15,00,000.00
3	Software	₹	20,00,000.00
4	License for Software	₹	12,00,000.00
5	AMC for Software	₹	15,00,000.00
6	Customisation, Implementation and Support	₹	79,90,125.00
	TOTAL	**₹**	**1,66,90,125.00**

Figure 2.19: *Bid price calculated*

Budget at completion

We will now consider that we have won the bid at the bid price we calculated. Customers usually negotiate against the bid price and ask for discounts, so we are at the stage where the project is ours and we have to execute it.

For the purpose of simplicity, we will consider that our project manager is assigned the task of customizing the software, deploying all the systems, and making the system go live. Essentially, we have taken away the responsibility of supplying the hardware and software from the project manager. So, the project manager only needs to look at the manpower cost of our project. So, our project manager has Rs.48,42,500.00 (Rupees forty-eight lakhs forty-two thousand and five hundred only) to complete the project. This figure is called the **Budget At Completion (BAC)**. BAC is the total budget allocated for the project.

First, let's compute the cost of each task that we must perform. This is given in *figure 2.20*. The amounts against each task are the BAC for the task. If the tasks are completed within their BAC, they would be completed within budget. Otherwise, they would overshoot their allocated budget.

Task ID	Task Description	Number of Resources	Number of Calendar Days	Predecessor	GRADE wise resource required						GRADE wise cost in thousands						Task Cost
					I	II	III	IV	V	VI	I	II	III	IV	V	VI	
A	Purchase Hardware	4	5					2	2		-	-	-	-	75.00	100.00	1,75,000.00
B	Purchase Software	4	5					2	2		-	-	-	-	75.00	100.00	1,75,000.00
C	Install Hardware	2	15	A	1			1			30.00	-	-	-	112.50	-	1,42,500.00
D	Create Prototype & Install Software	3	25	B,C	1			1	1		50.00	-	-	125.00	187.50	-	3,62,500.00
E	Customise Software	5	60	D			2	2	2	1	-	-	480.00	-	900.00	600.00	19,80,000.00
F	Migrate Data	3	25	D,E	1	1		1			-	75.00	100.00	-	187.50	-	3,62,500.00
G	Deploy Solution	3	10	F	1	1		1			20.00	30.00	-	-	75.00	-	1,25,000.00
H	Project Management Activities	3	50				1	1		1	-	-	200.00	250.00	-	500.00	9,50,000.00
I	Quality Assurance Activities	3	30				1	1		1	-	-	120.00	150.00	-	300.00	5,70,000.00
		225			3	2	5	3	10	7	100.00	105.00	900.00	525.00	1,612.50	1,600.00	

TOTAL COST: ₹ 48,42,500.00

Figure 2.20: Task-wise cost

Creating Gantt chart for the project

Gantt charts are one the oldest forms of graphical representations of a project plan and have been in use since World War 1. Gantt charts are named after *Henry L Gantt*. *Mr. Gantt* developed these charts to help with scheduling and better management of supplies and logistics during World War 1.

Gantt charts represent each task by a bar that extends from the time the task begins till the task ends. Each task has two bars: one for the planned duration and one for the actual duration. We can use a Gantt chart to figure out the progress made in the project against the plan that was laid out for it.

The plan for our project is shown in the Gantt chart in *figure 2.21*:

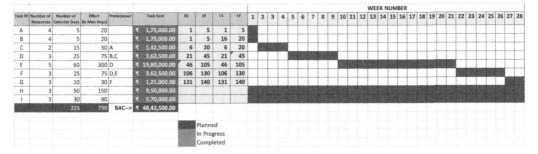

Figure 2.21: Gantt chart of the plan for the project

Note that project management activities (task H) and quality assurance activities (task I) are carried out throughout the project.

We will add the number of resources for each period the task is being executed to the Gantt chart in *figure 2.21*. This will give us the **Resource Loading Chart**, as shown in *figure 2.22*:

Task ID	Number of Resources	Number of Calendar Days	Effort (in Man Days)	Predecessor	Task Cost	ES	EF	LS	LF	1	2	3	4	5	6	7	8	9	10	11	12	13	14	15	16	17	18	19	20	21	22	23	24	25	26	27	28
A	4	5	20		₹ 1,75,000.00	1	5	1	5	4																											
B	4	5	20		₹ 1,75,000.00	1	5	16	20	4																											
C	2	15	30	A	₹ 1,42,500.00	6	20	6	20		2	2	2																								
D	3	25	75	B,C	₹ 3,62,500.00	21	45	21	45					3	3	3	3	3																			
E	5	60	300	D	₹ 19,80,000.00	46	105	46	105										5	5	5	5	5	5	5	5	5	5	5	5							
F	3	25	75	D,E	₹ 3,62,500.00	106	130	106	130																						3	3	3	3	3		
G	3	10	30	F	₹ 1,25,000.00	131	140	131	140																											3	3
H	3	50	150		₹ 9,50,000.00					1.1	1.1	1.1	1.1	1.1	1.1	1.1	1.1	1.1	1.1	1.1	1.1	1.1	1.1	1.1	1.1	1.1	1.1	1.1	1.1	1.1	1.1	1.1	1.1	1.1	1.1	1.1	1.1
I	3	30	90		₹ 5,70,000.00					0.6	0.6	0.6	0.6	0.6	0.6	0.6	0.6	0.6	0.6	0.6	0.6	0.6	0.6	0.6	0.6	0.6	0.6	0.6	0.6	0.6	0.6	0.6	0.6	0.6	0.6	0.6	0.6
	225		790	BAC-->	₹ 48,42,500.00			Resources per Week -->		10	4	4	4	5	5	5	5	5	7	7	7	7	7	7	7	7	7	7	7	5	5	5	5	5	5	5	5

Planned
In Progress
Completed

Figure 2.22: *Gantt chart with resource loading details*

For the sake of simplicity, we will assume that the resources are assigned uniformly across all the weeks of the project for tasks H and I. So, for task H, we consume an effort of 150 man-days over 140 days (or 28 weeks). This works out to (150/140) = 1.071 resources per week. And for task I, we consume an effort of 90 man-days over 140 days (or 28 weeks). This works out to (90/140) = 0.643 resources per week.

Figure 2.23 shows the resource loading chart as a graph. The week numbers are shown on the X-axis, and the number of resources required each week on the Y-axis:

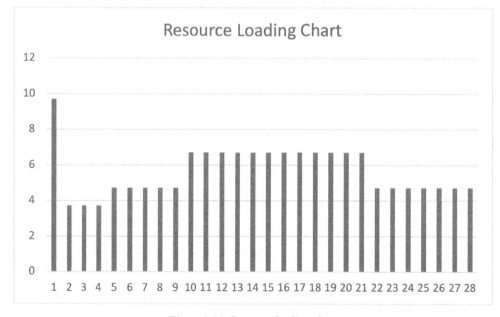

Figure 2.23: *Resource loading chart*

The resource loading chart should be such that the project should have less resources initially. This is because a small team usually starts to understand the project. Resources should be added as the project progresses, and they should be released from the project as it ends. So, the resource loading chart in *figure 2.23* is pretty much a perfect one.

Blended rate

In *figure 2.10*, note that we calculated the amount of money required for completing every task. While doing so, we calculated the amount of money required for utilizing resources from every grade separately. At that stage, it was important to calculate the amount for every grade to come to an accurate estimate of the amount of money required.

However, we must know the status of the task and the project once the project enters the execution phase. It is less important to know who performed the task from the project monitoring perspective; this information is important from other perspectives, like human resource management. Considering this, we can dilute the information regarding who performed the task and focus on where we are with respect to task completion.

Now, we know the amount of money required to perform each task (we have calculated this). We also know the total effort required to perform the task (we estimated this). So, if we divide the total money required to perform the task by the total effort required for the task, we get a monetary rate at which we require the resources for the task. This rate at which we require resources for a task, irrespective of the individual rates of the resources, is called the **blended rate**. So, the blended rate is a single rate which is the average amount for acquiring resources for performing a task.

When a company subcontracts work to another company, the rate fixed per resource is generally the blended rate across all levels of the resources used on the project.

Figure 2.24 shows the blended rates calculated for each task:

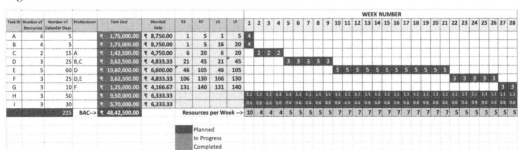

Figure 2.24: *Blended rate for every task calculated*

For example, we need two resources in grade VI and two resources in grade V for task A. The cost of grade VI resources is (2 resources * 5 days * Rs. 10,000 per resource per day) = Rs. 1,00,000.00. The cost of grade V resources is (2 resources * 5 days * Rs. 7,500 per resource per day) = Rs. 75,000.00.

So, the total cost of performing task A is (Rs. 1,00,000 + Rs. 75,000) = Rs. 1,75,000.00. Now, the total effort required to perform task A is (4 resources * 5 man-days) = 20 man-days. So, the blended rate for task A is (Rs. 1,75,000 / 20 man-days) = Rs. 8,750 per man-day.

Planned value

At any point of time in the project, we would like to know what should have been our status. We can get an estimate for this by calculating the **Planned Value** (**PV**).

Let's take an example. Suppose we want to know what our status at the end of week 1 should be. According to our Gantt chart (as shown in *figure 2.22*), we plan to complete task A and task B at the end of week 1. In completing task A and task B, we plan to consume four resources for task A at the rate Rs.8,750 per resource per day and four resources for task B at the rate of Rs.8,750 per resource per day. In other words, task A and task B should be 100% complete and all the remaining tasks should be 0% complete at the end of week 1.

Now, we get this if we compute the amount of money we planned to spend by the end of week 1:

Task	Money to spend (formula)	Amount
A	4 resources * 5 days * Rs. 8,750/resource/day	Rs. 1,75,000.00
B	4 resources * 5 days * Rs. 8,750/resource/day	Rs. 1,75,000.00
H	1.071 resources * 5 days * Rs. 6,333.33/resource/day	Rs. 33,914.98
I	0.643 resources * 5 days * Rs. 6,333.33/resource/day	Rs. 20,361.66
TOTAL		**Rs. 4,04,276.64**

Table 2.1: Planned value calculation for the project at the end of week 1

So, the planned value for the project at the end of week 1 is Rs.4,04,276.64.

Dividing the planned value that we have computed by the BAC will give us the percentage of the project that we aim to complete by the end of week 1:

Planned Percentage Completion = Planned Value / BAC

We know that the BAC is Rs.48,42,500.00, so the planned percentage completion at the end of week 1 is (Rs.4,04,276.64 / Rs.48,42,500.00) = 8.3%.

Similarly, we can calculate the planned percentage completion at the end of each week of the project, as shown in *figure 2.25*:

WEEK NUMBER																											
1	2	3	4	5	6	7	8	9	10	11	12	13	14	15	16	17	18	19	20	21	22	23	24	25	26	27	28
4																											
4																											
		2	2	2																							
					3	3	3	3	3																		
										5	5	5	5	5	5	5	5	5	5	5							
																						3	3	3	3	3	
																										3	3
1.071	1.071	1.071	1.071	1.071	1.071	1.071	1.071	1.071	1.071	1.071	1.071	1.071	1.071	1.071	1.071	1.071	1.071	1.071	1.071	1.071	1.071	1.071	1.071	1.071	1.071	1.071	1.0714
0.643	0.643	0.643	0.643	0.643	0.643	0.643	0.643	0.643	0.643	0.643	0.643	0.643	0.643	0.643	0.643	0.643	0.643	0.643	0.643	0.643	0.643	0.643	0.643	0.643	0.643	0.643	0.6429
10	4	4	4	5	5	5	5	5	7	7	7	7	7	7	7	7	7	7	7	5	5	5	5	5	5	5	5
8.3%	10.5%	12.6%	14.7%	17.3%	19.9%	22.5%	25.1%	27.7%	32.3%	36.8%	41.3%	45.9%	50.4%	54.9%	59.4%	64.0%	68.5%	73.0%	77.6%	82.1%	84.7%	87.3%	89.9%	92.6%	95.2%	97.6%	100.0%

Figure 2.25: Planned percentage completion calculated for all weeks of the project

There are cases where the people monitoring the project will have the figure regarding the planned percentage completion and would like to compute the PV. In that case, the PV can be computed as follows:

*PV = Planned percentage completion * BAC*

Suppose (in our case) the planned percentage complete is 30%, then PV can be calculated as follows:

PV = 30% * Rs. 48,42,500 = Rs. 14,52,750.00

We can use one more method to compute the PV. If we compute the PV for each task at a point of time and add all the values, we will get the PV for the project at that point of time. For example, we compute the PV at the end of week 6 for the tasks A, B, C, D, H, and I and add all these PVs to get the PV for the project at the end of week 6.

Task	Money to spend (formula)	Planned Value
A	4 resources * 1 weeks * 5 days/week * Rs. 8,750/resource/day	Rs. 1,75,000.00
B	4 resources * 1 weeks * 5 days/week * Rs. 8,750/resource/day	Rs. 1,75,000.00
C	2 resources * 3 weeks * 5 days/week * Rs. 4,750/resource/day	Rs. 1,42,500.00
D	3 resources * 2 weeks * 5 days/week * Rs. 4,833.33/resource/day	Rs. 1,44,999.90
H	1.071 resources * 6 weeks * 5 days/week * Rs. 6,333.33/resource/day	Rs. 2,03,489.89
I	0.643 resources * 6 weeks * 5 days/week * Rs. 6,333.33/resource/day	Rs. 1,22,169.94
TOTAL		Rs. 9,63,159.73

Table 2.2: Planned value at the end of week 6

Earned value

At any point of time, we would like to know where we are in the project. We can get an estimate for this by calculating the **Earned Value (EV)**, which is the value we have got from the project till a point of time in the project.

Our progress in the project as of week 6 is as shown in *figure 2.26*:

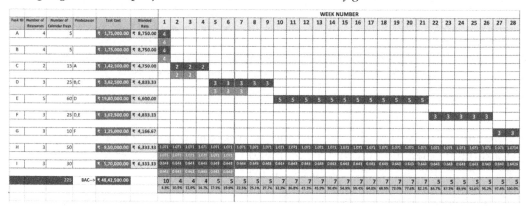

Figure 2.26: *Project progress as of week 6 (green bars indicate completed activities)*

Figure 2.26 shows that tasks A and B are completed, task C is 2/3 completed, and task D is 3/5 completed as of week 6. Also, tasks H and I are progressing as per plan.

We can now calculate the value earned from the completed task as of week 6, as shown in *table 2.3*. The value of the completed tasks as of week 6 is the EV of the project as of week 6.

Task	Value Earned from completed tasks (formula)	Earned Value
A	4 resources * 1 weeks * 5 days/week * Rs. 8,750/resource/day	Rs. 1,75,000.00
B	4 resources * 1 weeks * 5 days/week * Rs. 8,750/resource/day	Rs. 1,75,000.00
C	2 resources * 2 weeks * 5 days/week * Rs. 4,750/resource/day	Rs. 95,000.00
D	3 resources * 3 weeks * 5 days/week * Rs. 4,833.33/resource/day	Rs. 2,17,499.85
H	1.071 resources * 6 weeks * 5 days/week * Rs. 6,333.33/resource/day	Rs. 2,03,489.89
I	0.643 resources * 6 weeks * 5 days/week * Rs. 6,333.33/resource/day	Rs. 1,22,169.94
	TOTAL	**Rs. 9,88,159.68**

Table 2.3: *Earned value at the end of week 6*

So, under the project position given in *figure 2.26*, the EV for the project at the end of week 6 is Rs.9,88,159.68.

We can compute the actual percentage of the project completion from the EV as follows:

Actual Completion Percentage = Earned Value / BAC

So, we can calculate our project's actual completion percentage at the end of week 6 as (Rs.9,88,159.68 / Rs.48,42,500.00) = 20.4%.

Many times, the project management team has the value of the actual completion percentage of the project. We can compute the **Earned Value (EV)** from the actual completion percentage as follows:

EV = Actual Completion Percentage * BAC

So, if our project is 45% complete at the end of week 12, then our project's EV at the end of week 12 would be (45% * Rs. 48,42,500) = Rs. 21,79,125.00.

Actual cost

When we calculated the EV, we considered that we consumed the resources as they were planned to be consumed. However, generally, we consume resources differently during the actual project execution from what we would have planned. We get the **Actual Cost (AC)** when we consider the actual consumption of resources and compute the cost.

Suppose we consumed the resources as shown in *figure 2.27* in our project at the end of week 6.

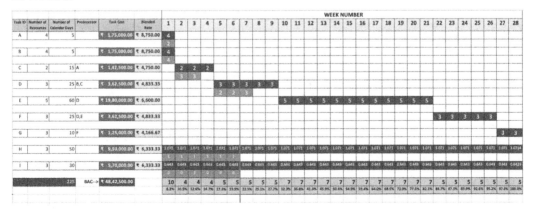

Figure 2.27: Actual consumption of resources as of week 6 (shown in the green bars)

We can see that we consumed two resources to perform task A instead of four resources. We consumed three resources in week 2 and week 3 to perform task C, two resources in week 5 and 6, and three resources in week 7 to perform task D. Lastly, we can see that we consumed one resource to perform task H in weeks 1 through 6 and two resources in week 3 to perform task I.

Based on these consumptions, we can compute the AC as shown in *table 2.4*:

Task	Actual consumption (formula)	Actual Cost
A	2 resources * 1 weeks * 5 days/week * Rs. 8,750/resource/day	Rs. 87,500.00
B	4 resources * 1 weeks * 5 days/week * Rs. 8,750/resource/day	Rs. 1,75,000.00
C	3 resources * 2 weeks * 5 days/week * Rs. 4,750/resource/day	Rs. 1,42,500.00
D	((2 resources * 2 weeks) + (3 resources * 1 weeks)) * 5 days/week * Rs. 4,833.33/resource/day	Rs. 1,69,166.55
H	1 resources * 6 weeks * 5 days/week * Rs. 6,333.33/resource/day	Rs. 1,89,999.90
I	2 resources * 1 weeks * 5 days/week * Rs. 6,333.33/resource/day	Rs. 63,333.30
	TOTAL	**Rs. 8,27,499.75**

Table 2.4: Actual cost at the end of week 6

Note: Reliable value of Actual Cost can be obtained from an organization's finance department. Apart from resource cost, there can be costs attributed to the project by the finance department. However, rough figures can be calculated by the project management team using systems like timesheet management systems.

Schedule variance

Schedule Variance (SV) is the difference between earned value and planned value. SV indicates how much ahead or behind schedule the project is.

Schedule Variance (SV) = Earned Value (EV) – Planned Value (PV)

For our project, the SV as of week 6 is (Rs.9,88,159.68 – Rs.9,69,159.73) = Rs.18,999.95.

We can see that SV can take a value that is 0 or >0 or <0. If the SV is 0, then the project is on schedule. If the SV is greater than 0, then the project is ahead of schedule. If the SV is less than 0, then the project is behind schedule.

In our case, the project is ahead of schedule as of week 6.

Cost variance

Cost Variance (CV) is the difference between earned value and actual cost. CV indicates how much over or under budget the project is.

Cost Variance (CV) = Earned Value (EV) – Actual Cost (AC)

For our project, the CV as of week 6 is (Rs.9,88,159.68 – Rs.8,27,499.75) = Rs.1,60,659.93.

We can see that CV can take a value that is 0 or >0 or <0. If the CV is 0, then the project is in budget. If the CV is greater than 0, then the project is under budget. If the CV is less than 0, then the project is over budget.

In our case, the project is under budget as of week 6. In other words, the project has used less money than what was budgeted as of week 6.

Schedule performance index

Schedule Performance Index (SPI) is the ratio between earned value and planned value. SPI indicates whether the progress of the project is in conformance with the plan.

Schedule Performance Index (SPI) = Earned Value (EV) / Planned Value (PV)

SPI can take a value of 1 or <1 or >1. If SPI is 1, then the project is on target. If SPI is greater than 1, then the project is ahead of the planned target. If SPI is less than 1, then the project is behind the planned target.

In our case, SPI at the end of week 6 is (Rs. 9,88,159.68 / Rs. 9,69,159.73) = 1.0196. So, the project is ahead of the planned target as of week 6.

Cost performance index

Cost Performance Index (CPI) is the ratio between earned value and actual cost. CPI indicates the conformance of the actual work completed in the project against the actual cost incurred by the project:

Cost Performance Index (CPI) = Earned Value (EV) / Actual Cost (AC)

CPI can take a value of 1 or <1 or >1. If CPI is 1, then the project is on budget. If CPI is greater than 1, then the project is under budget (i.e., the project has spent less money than the value of the work completed). If CPI is less than 1, then the project is over budget (i.e., the project has spent more money as compared to the value of the work completed).

For our project, CPI at the end of week 6 is (Rs. 9,88,159.68 / Rs. 8,27,499.75) = 1.1942. So, the project has produced more value as compared to the money spent on it as of week 6.

Estimate at completion

At any point of time in the project, we can estimate the amount at which the project can be completed. This amount is called the **Estimate At Completion (EAC)**. EAC is calculated based on the assumption that the project will progress till the end the same way it is progressing at that point of time.

The EAC can be calculated by dividing BAC by CPI:

$EAC = BAC / CPI$

For our project, we can say that the EAC at the end of week 6 can be expected to be (Rs. 48,42,500.00 / 1.1942) = Rs. 40,55,182.19. So, given the current progress of the project, it seems like we can complete the project utilizing less than what was budgeted for it.

Note that the project progresses at different rates at different points. So, to be realistic, we should calculate the EAC routinely to get an estimate of where the project might end. Preventive or corrective measures should be taken based on the EAC.

Estimate to complete

At any point of time in the project, we can estimate the amount required to complete the project. This amount is called the **Estimate To Complete (ETC)**. ETC is calculated based on the assumption that the project will continue till the end the same way it is progressing at that point of time.

The ETC can be calculated by dividing (BAC – EV) by CPI:

$EAC = (BAC - EV) / CPI$

So, for our project, the ETC at of the end of week 6 is ((Rs. 48,42,500.00 – Rs. 9,88,159.68) / 1.1942 = Rs. 32,27,550.09. So, we still need this amount to complete the project, given that the project progresses in the same manner as it is currently progressing.

Intuitively, we can derive the following formula:

Expected at Completion (EAC) = Actual Cost (AC) + Estimate to Complete (ETC)

Variance at completion

At any point of time in the project, we can estimate the difference between the budget in which the project was planned to be completed (BAC) and the budget in which the project is expected to be completed (EAC). This amount is called the **Variance at Completion (VAC)**. VAC is calculated based on the assumption that the project will continue like it is progressing at that point of time until the end.

$VAC = BAC - EAC$

For our project, the VAC at the end of week 6 is (Rs. 48,42,500.00 – Rs. 40,55,182.19) = Rs. 7,87,317.81.

If VAC is greater than 0, the project is expected to consume less than the budgeted amount. If VAC is less than 0, then the project is expected to consume more than the budget.

To complete performance index

To Complete Performance Index (TCPI) is the performance efficiency required to complete the project at a cost target. It is the future cost performance that must be achieved to meet the management objective for the project.

If TC is the target cost objective, then TCPI can be calculated as follows:

$$TCPI = \frac{BAC - EV}{TC - AC}$$

Here, BAC is the budget at completion, EV is the earned value at a given point of the project, and AC is the actual cost at a given point in the project.

If the cost objective is to complete the project at BAC, then TCPI is calculated as follows:

$$TCPI = \frac{BAC - EV}{BAC - AC}$$

For our project, we can calculate TCPI at BAC at the end of week 6 as ((Rs. 48,42,500.00 – Rs. 9,88,159.68) / (Rs. 48,42,500.00 – Rs. 8,27,499.75)) = 0.96.

If the cost objective is to complete the project at the current EAC, then TCPI is calculated as follows:

$$TCPI = \frac{BAC - EV}{EAC - AC}$$

For our project, we can calculate TCPI at EAC at the end of week 6 as ((Rs. 48,42,500.00 – Rs. 9,88,159.68) / (Rs. 40,55,182.19 – Rs. 8,27,499.75)) = 1.19.

For a healthy project, TCPI should always be close to 1.0. If TCPI is less than 1.0, then the target should be relatively easy to achieve. If TCPI is 1.0, then the target can be met if the current level of performance is maintained. If TCPI is greater than 1.0, then improvement in performance is required to achieve the management objective.

Percent complete index – Budget costs

Percent Complete Index – Budget Costs (PCI-B) is a reliability estimate of the project progress. Reliability of a project increases as PCI-B increases. PCI-B is a very good indicator of how much of the project has been completed. It is the percentage of work in a project that has been completed to date in terms of the budget and is calculated as follows:

PCI-B = EV / BAC

For our project, PCI-B at the end of week 6 is (Rs. 9,88,159.68 / Rs. 48,42,500.00) = 20.4%.

Percent complete index – Actual costs

Percent Complete Index – Actual Costs (PCI-C) is a reliability estimate of the project progress. A project's reliability increases as PCI-C increases. PCI-C is a very good indicator of how much of the project has been completed. It is the percentage of work in a project that has been completed to date in terms of the revised project budget. PCI-C is calculated as follows.

PCI-C = AC / EAC

For our project, PCI-C at the end of week 6 is (Rs. 8,27,499.75 / Rs. 40,55,182.19) = 20.4%.

Conclusion

In this chapter, we started our discussions around all the components required for setting the stage to apply earned value method for project management. We discussed how projects can be priced using cost-based pricing. Once we have the price of the project, we can derive the cost at which we would aim to execute the project to make appropriate levels of profit.

We discussed the components of the earned value method once the essential components were in place. We discussed how to calculate the planned and earned values and derived indicators of project health using these values. We saw that these indicators give critical information regarding where the project is headed and what needs to be done (if required) to bring the project on track.

In the next chapter, we will take a detour into mathematics. We will explore linear programming problems and discuss how to solve them.

Points to remember

- BAC is the Budget At Completion
- PV = Planned Completion Percentage * BAC
- EV = Actual Completed Percentage * BAC
- SV = EV – PV
- CV = EV – AC
- SPI = EV / PV
- CPI = EV / AC
- EAC = BAC / CPI
- ETC = (BAC – EV) / CPI
- VAC = BAC – EAC
- PCI-B = EV / BAC
- PCI-C = AC / EAC

Multiple choice questions

1. **If SPI is 0.95 and CPI is 1.04, it implies that:**
   a. The project ahead of schedule and over the budget
   b. The project behind schedule and over the budget
   c. The project behind schedule but within the budget
   d. The project ahead of schedule but within the budget

2. **If AC is Rs. 10,000 and ETC is Rs. 90,000, then EAC =:**
   a. Rs. 80,000
   b. Rs. 1,00,000
   c. Rs. 9,000
   d. It cannot be determined

3. **If PV is Rs. 10,000 and EV is Rs. 12,000, then SPI =:**
   a. 1.2
   b. 0.83
   c. 2
   d. It cannot be determined

4. **If AC is Rs. 10,000 and EV is Rs. 12,000, then CPI =:**

    a. 1.2

    b. 0.83

    c. 2

    d. It cannot be determined

5. **If BAC is Rs. 1,00,000 and CPI is 0.9, then EAC =:**

    a. Rs. 90,000.00

    b. 0.83

    c. Rs. 1,11,111.11

    d. It cannot be determined

Answers

1. c
2. b
3. a
4. a
5. c

Questions

1. Calculate PV, EV, AC, SPI, and CPI f or the project given in the *figure 2.28* at the end of week 12. What conclusions can you draw about the project?

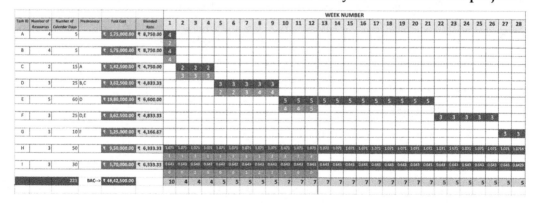

Figure 2.28: Question 1

2. Calculate PV, EV, AC, SPI, and CPI for the project given in *figure 2.29* at the end of week 12. What conclusions can you draw about the project?

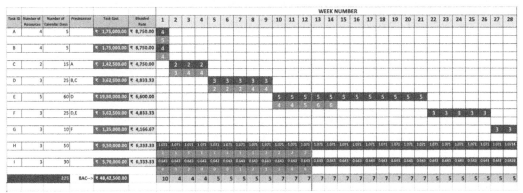

Figure 2.29: Question 2

Key terms

- **OEM**: Original Equipment Manufacturer
- **AMC**: Annual Maintenance Contract
- **RFP**: Request For Proposal
- **BAC**: Budget At Completion
- **PV**: Planned Value
- **EV**: Earned Value
- **AC**: Actual Cost
- **SV**: Schedule Variance
- **CV**: Cost Variance
- **SPI**: Schedule Performance Index
- **CPI**: Cost Performance Index
- **EAC**: Estimate at Completion
- **ETC**: Estimate To Complete
- **VAC**: Variance At Completion
- **TCPI**: To Complete Performance Index

CHAPTER 3
Linear Programing Problems

In the previous two chapters, we discussed how to schedule and cost a project. We noticed that both these aspects of project management are mathematical. So, to optimize the aspects of time and cost in project management, we can set them up as mathematical problems.

When we need to optimize any situation in mathematics, i.e., we need to maximize or minimize a quantity, we set up the problem as a linear programming problem and then solve it. By doing so, we may get a solution or conclude that the problem has no solution. In this chapter, we will first discuss how to set up a problem as a linear programming problem, and then we will understand how to solve these problems.

We will discuss practical business problems that we will convert to a linear programming problem and try to find a solution. We will also discuss elementary methods that can be used for simple problems. Additionally, we will familiarize ourselves with the essential components of linear programming problems and discuss the tools available to solve these problems.

We will discuss the concepts using a simple problem, and then we will discuss a more intense problem.

Structure

We will discuss the following topics in this chapter:

- Optimization problems
- Graphical solution
- Solving LPP using Microsoft Excel
    - Installing solver
    - Setting up the LPP on Microsoft Excel
    - Setting up solver for the LPP
- Bill printing problem

Objectives

After studying this unit, you will be able to formulate an optimizing requirement as a linear programming problem. You will also be able to solve linear programming problems using Microsoft Excel.

Optimization problem

We come across optimization problems almost every day and in every sphere of life, be a personal or professional setup. Though you may not act on it, the thought of how you can optimize your monthly expenses may cross your mind. When we commute to office, we should look for how we can minimize the time required to reach the office and come back home. In office, if you have profit and loss responsibilities, you must be looking to maximize your department's profit. When in business, we come across situations where we need to choose between various projects to invest in to maximize profit. Food delivery companies work on how to minimize the cost of delivering the orders to maximize their profits. The examples are endless. If you look carefully, every situation provides an optimization problem.

In optimization problems, we either maximize or minimize the quantity subject to some constraints. The quantity can be time, money, pressure, volume, and such. Any quantity that can be computed mathematically can be subject to maximization or minimization.

If you think carefully, every optimization problem can be expressed mathematically. This is because the quantity to be optimized can be expressed numerically regardless of whether it is a business, scientific, or personal setup. Once we can express the quantity to be optimized numerically, we can also formulate the constraints numerically. So, we have a set of equations to be solved.

Let's understand this with an example.

Suppose we have a small-scale garment factory that produces shirts and blouses, and the production process has two steps: cutting and stitching. Now, suppose the time required to cut and stitch a shirt and blouse is as shown in *figure 3.1*:

Article	Time required in hours	
	Cutting	Stitching
Shirt	1	3
Blouse	2	2

Figure 3.1: Time required for cutting and stitching shirt and blouse

Suppose the profit from one shirt and one blouse is $10 and $12, respectively. So, the updated table looks as shown in *figure 3.2*:

Article	Time required in hours		Profit per unit
	Cutting	Stitching	
Shirt	1	3	$ 10.00
Blouse	2	2	$ 12.00

Figure 3.2: Profit figures added to the assumptions

Further, suppose that the factory has two workers in the cutting department and three workers in the stitching department. Each worker can work for 10 hours per day. So, all our assumptions are provided in *figure 3.3*:

Article	Time required in hours		Profit per unit
	Cutting	Stitching	
Shirt	1	3	$ 10.00
Blouse	2	2	$ 12.00
Number of workers	2	3	
Hours per day per worker	10	10	
Work Hours / day	20	30	

Figure 3.3: Work hour assumption added

Note: We have assumed that a worker needs 1 hour to cut a shirt. Similarly, we have assumed the time required for other activities stated previously. In a normal factory environment, data is collected over a period (generally, this is a reasonable amount of time, like 50 or 100 days or even a year) to check the productivity. A factory sets its benchmark based on these observations. Note that the productivity figures include the time required for breaks like lunch, tea, late arrival, early departure, and such.

In this factory setup, we want to determine the maximum profit that can be generated per day. In other words, we want to determine how many shirts and how many blouses have to be produced such that the profit is the maximum.

Let's now analyze what we have got.

We have to maximize the profit for this factory. The profit is generated from the number of shirts and number of blouses produced. Let's assume that the number of shirts produced per day is , and number of blouses produced per day is . Now, the profit per day can be calculated as follows:

$$Profit\ per\ day = 10x_1 + 12x_2 \qquad\qquad - (1)$$

We have to maximize the profit per day. The function that has to be maximized or minimized is called the **objective function**. In our case, the function stated in (1) is the objective function.

However, we have some constraints in terms of the time, as stated in *figure 3.3*. The maximum hours available for cutting and stitching are 20 and 30 per day, respectively.

The number of shirts and blouses that can be cut per day is given by . This figure is in terms of hours. This number must be less than or equal to 20 as we have only 20 hours per day for cutting, so we have one constraint, as follows:

$$x_1 + 2x_2 \le 20 \qquad\qquad - (2)$$

The number of shirts and blouses that can be stitched per day is given by 3. This figure is in terms of hours. This number must be less than or equal to 30 as we have only 30 hours per day for stitching, so we have one more constraint, as follows:

$$3x_1 + 2x_2 \le 30 \qquad\qquad - (3)$$

Now, we have to produce some shirts and blouses. So, must be greater than or equal to 0. The same is the case for . So, we have two more constraints, as follows:

$$x_1 \ge 0 \qquad\qquad\qquad -(4)$$

$$x_2 \ge 0 \qquad\qquad\qquad -(5)$$

So, we have our optimization problem, as shown here:

Maximize $10x_1 + 12x_2$

Subject to

$$x_1 + 2x_2 \le 20$$

$$3x_1 + 2x_2 \le 30$$

$$x_1 + \ge 0$$

$$x_2 + \ge 0$$

Note that all the equations we are dealing with are linear, so these problems are called **Linear Programming Problems (LPP)**.

Note: We have considered a small-scale industry so that the numbers to consider are small. Also, we have kept only two variables in and so that we can represent the complete problem in a two-dimensional graph.

Graphical solution

We have our optimization problem. First, we will solve this problem using graphs. We can do this for our present problem as we have only two variables and can represent the problem on a two-dimensional graph. This method cannot be used when the number of variables increases.

To solve the problem, we take each constraint and graph it. Now, the constraints in our case are inequalities, so we remove the inequalities and consider them to be equations. So, we will consider the inequality

$$x_1 + 2x_2 \le 20 \qquad \text{to be}$$

$$x_1 + 2x_2 = 20 \qquad \text{- (A) and graph it.}$$

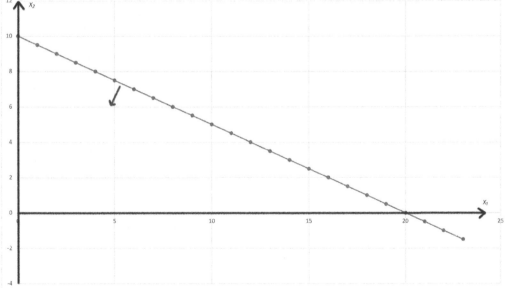

***Figure 3.4**: Graph of equation (A)*

In *figure 3.4*, the green arrow points to the direction of the inequality.

Next, we will plot the second constraint:

$$3x_1 + 2x_2 \le 30$$

We will get the following on converting it to an equality:

$$3x_1 + 2x_2 = 30 \qquad\qquad\qquad - (B)$$

On plotting equation B, we obtain a graph as shown in *figure 3.5.*:

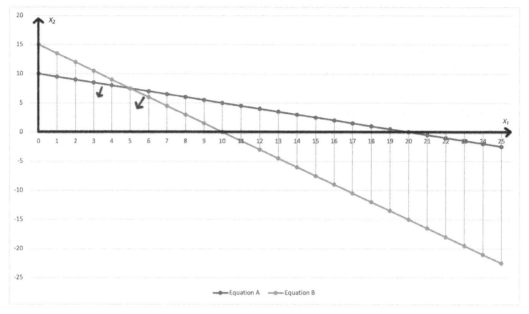

Figure 3.5: *Graph of equation (B) included*

In *figure 3.5*, the green arrows show the direction of the inequalities.

We have two more inequalities requiring and to be positive or zero.

So, we can take the four constraints and plot the feasible solution area, as shown in *figure 3.6*. The feasible solution will lie in the area bound by the points A, B, C, and D.

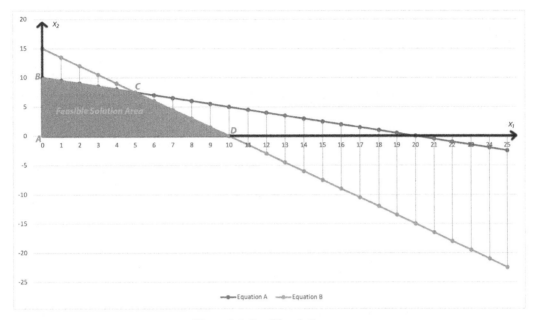

Figure 3.6: *Feasible solution area*

So, the solution to our maximization problem will lie somewhere in the area bound by the points A, B, C, and D (or the feasible solution area). Now, there are infinite points in the area ABCD. We cannot test all the points in this area to determine the optimum solution, so we need a method to arrive at a solution quickly.

We will determine the direction in which the objective function increases (this is because we are maximizing our objective function in this example. If we were minimizing our objective function, we would determine the direction in which the objective function decreases). We will start with any two arbitrary values of profit, say $50 and $90. Here, the profit of $90 is greater than the profit of $50.

Essentially, this means that we need to find the lines for the following equations:

$$10x_1 + 12\ x_2 = 50 \qquad - lineX$$

$$10x_1 + 12\ x_2 = 90 \qquad - lineY$$

Figure 3.7: shows lineX and lineY plotted:

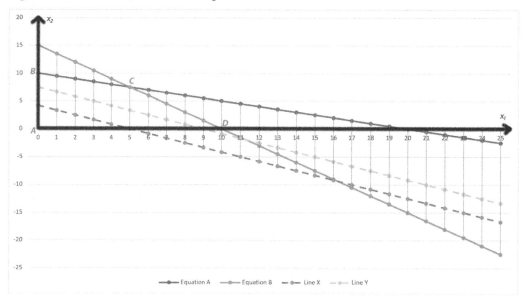

Figure 3.7: *Lines plotted for profits of $50 and $90*

We can see the direction of the increase of the profit from the brown dashed line to the yellow dashed line. From this, we can infer that the maximizing point will be point C. Now, point C has = 5, so we can find = (20 -)/2 = (20 – 5)/2 = 15/2 = 7.5 (we obtain this from equation A).

So, the optimum solution is to manufacture 5 shirts and 7.5 blouses. The maximum profit is ($10 * 5 + $12 * 7.5) = ($50 + $90) = $140.

However, we cannot manufacture 7.5 blouses. The number we manufacture should be a whole number. So, we can decide to manufacture 7 blouses, but we need to check whether the point = 5 and = 7 lies in the feasible solution area. *Figure 3.7* shows that this point lies in the feasible solution area.

The daily profit generated if we manufacture 5 shirts and 7 blouses is ($10 * 5 + $12 * 7) = ($50 + $84) = $134. We can see that the profit is less than the maximum profit.

Solving LPP using Microsoft Excel

We can use the graphical method when we have only two variables. Even then, solving linear programming problems using graphical methods can be daunting. Getting into the mathematics of solving linear programming problems can be daunting for the scope of this book, so clearing the concepts of *what is an objective function, what are the variables to vary* and *what are the constraints are clear* will be sufficient.

Using these concepts, we will discuss how we can solve linear programming problems using Microsoft Excel. Microsoft Excel encapsulates the complete mathematics behind solving linear programming problems in its add-on tool called **Solver**. However, we must understand the concepts of linear programming problems to be able to set up a Solver to solve these problems.

Let's now look at how to solve the same problem with a graphical method using Solver.

Installing solver

We need to set up Solver before discussing how to solve linear programming problems using it. Solver is an add-on tool in Microsoft Excel and is not available by default.

You will see a screen as shown in *figure 3.8* when you invoke Microsoft Excel:

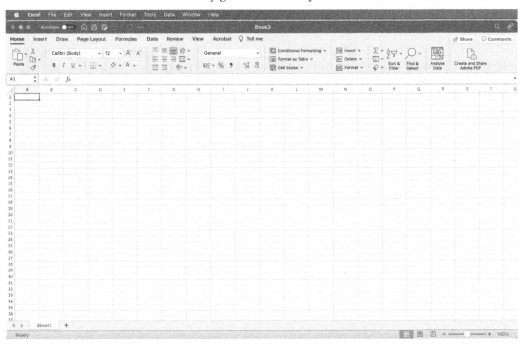

Figure 3.8: Microsoft Excel invoked on Apple Mac

Figure 3.8 shows the screen when Microsoft Excel is invoked on an Apple Mac machine. The screen would look different on a Microsoft Windows PC, but the method for adding and using Solver is the same in both Apple Mac and Microsoft Windows PC.

After invoking Microsoft Excel, click on the **Tools** menu option, as shown in *figure 3.9*:

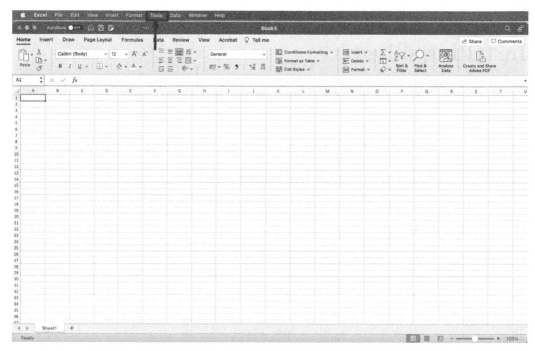

Figure 3.9: *Tools menu option pointed on Microsoft Excel*

Click on the **Excel Add-ins**... menu option under the **Tools** menu option, as shown in *figure 3.10*:

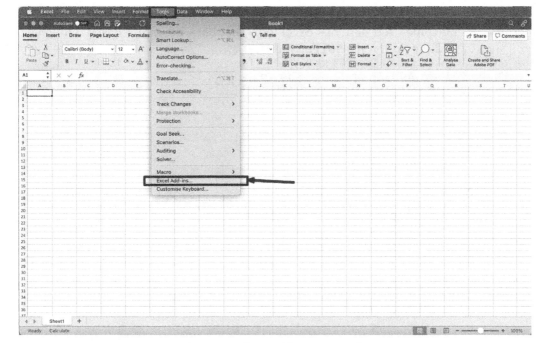

Figure 3.10: *Excel Add-ins menu option*

You will get a pop-up screen after clicking on the menu option, as shown in *figure 3.11*:

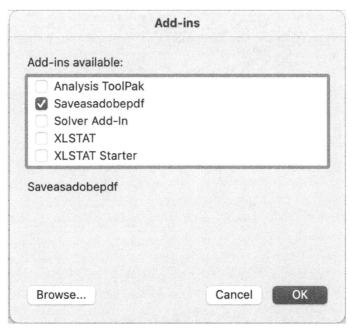

Figure 3.11: *Add-ins pop-up in Microsoft Excel*

The options in the Add-ins pop-up may be different on your computer. This is because the machine used here has Excel tools that have been purchased. However, you should find the option for **Solver Add-In**.

Check the **Solver Add-In** option, as shown in *figure 3.12*:

Figure 3.12: *Solver Add-In selected for inclusion in Microsoft Excel*

After selecting **Solver Add-In** for inclusion in Microsoft Excel, click on **OK**. You will be redirected to the Microsoft Excel screen, as shown in *figure 3.8*. On this screen, click on the **Data** tab, as illustrated in *figure 3.13*:

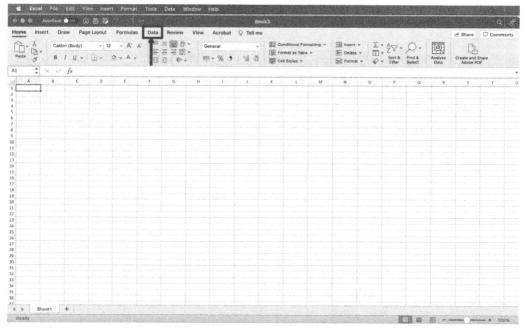

Figure 3.13: *The BLUE marker shows where to click to display the Data tab in Microsoft Excel*

The screen will look like this after invoking the **Data** tab:

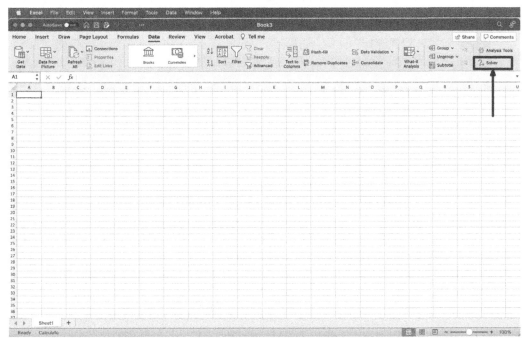

Figure 3.14: *Data tab of Microsoft Excel with the Solver tool*

In the **Data** tab, you can see the Solver tool, as shown in *figure 3.14* with the BLUE marker.

Setting up the LPP on Microsoft Excel

Now, let's set up our linear programming problem on Microsoft Excel. Our problem is restated here:

Maximize $10x_1 + 12x_2$

Subject to

$$x_1 + 2x_2 \leq 20$$

$$3x_1 + 2x_2 \leq 30$$

$$x_1 + \geq 0$$

$$x_2 + \geq 0$$

Figure 3.15 shows the planting of the problem on Microsoft Excel:

	Article	Number to manufacture	Time required in hours		Total Time Required		Profit per unit	Total Profit per Article
			Cutting	Stitching	Cutting	Stitching		
4	Shirt		1	3	0	0	$ 10.00	$ -
5	Blouse		2	2	0	0	$ 12.00	$ -
6		Number of workers	2	3				
7		Hours per day per worker	10	10			Total Profit ->	$ -
8		Work Hours / day	20	30			Function to Maximize	
10			Total Time per Process ->		0	0		
11					<=	<=		
12			Constraints ->		20	30		

Figure 3.15: *LPP problem planted on Microsoft Excel*

Let's understand the Microsoft Excel sheet in *figure 3.15*. In cells C4 and C5, we want the number of shirts and blouses to be manufactured per day. We do not know these figures upfront. We want these numbers such that the profit is maximum, so these are our variables to change. *With respect to the problem we have formulated, cell C4 is x_1 and cell C5 is x_2.*

We also know that we want x_1 and x_2 to be greater than or equal to 0.

In cells D4, D5, E4, and E5, we have the number of hours required for cutting and stitching one shirt and one blouse. For example, cell D4 contains the number of hours required for cutting one shirt.

We need to calculate the total hours we would need if we produced number of shirts. So, in cell F4, we will plant a formula to C4 * D4. In cell F5, we will plant the formula C5 * D5. In cell G4, we will plant the formula C4 * E4. Lastly, in cell G5, we will plant the formula C5 * E5.

In cell F10, we will compute the total number of hours required for the cutting process if number of shirts are manufactured per day. We can do this by planting the formula F4 + F5 in cell F10 (we can also plant the formula SUM(F4:F5) in cell F10 to get the same result). Similarly, we can compute the total number of hours required for stitching by planting the formula G4 + G5 in cell G10 (we can get the same result by planting the formula SUM(G4:G5) in cell G10).

In cells D8 and E8, we have computed the maximum number of hours available per day for the cutting and stitching processes. This is done by planting the formula D6 * D7 in cell D8 and the formula E6 * E7 in cell E8. We will just copy these values in cells F12 and G12 by planting the formula D8 in cell F12 and E8 in cell G12.

So, now we can visualize that we need the value in cell F10 to be less than or equal to the value in cell F12. Similarly, we need the value in cell G10 to be less than or equal to the value in cell G12. *So, these are our constraints.*

The profit we generate from one shirt is $10 and from one blouse is $12. We will put these figures in cells H4 and H5, so we can calculate the total profit from number of shirts by planting the formula C4 * H4 in cell I4. Similarly, we can calculate the total profit from number of blouses by planting the formula C5 * H5 in cell I5. We can now compute the total profit in cell I7 by planting the formula I4 + I5 (or SUM(I4:I5)). We must maximize the value in cell I7 by changing the values in cells C4 and C5. *So, cell I7 contains the objective function.*

So, we have all the components of the linear programming problem: the objective function, the constraints, and the variable to modify.

Figure 3.16 shows all the formulae set in the Microsoft Excel sheet:

	A	B	C	D	E	F	G	H	I
1									
2		**Article**	**Number to manufacture**	*Time required in hours*		*Total Time Required*		**Profit per unit**	Total Profit per Article
3				**Cutting**	**Stitching**	**Cutting**	**Stitching**		
4		Shirt		1	3	=D4*$C4	=E4*$C4	10	=H4*C4
5		Blouse		2	2	=D5*$C5	=E5*$C5	12	=H5*C5
6			Number of workers	2	3				
7			Hours per day per worker	10	10			Total Profit ->	=SUM(I4:I5)
8			Work Hours / day	=D7*D6	=E7*E6		*Function to Maximize*		
9									
10				Total Time per Process ->		=SUM(F4:F5)	=SUM(G4:G5)		
11						<=	<=		
12				Constraints ->	=D8	=E8			

Figure 3.16: *A view of the formulae set for the LPP*

Figure 3.17 shows the calculations when we set to manufacture four shirts and four blouses per day:

	A	B	C	D	E	F	G	H	I
1									
2		**Article**	**Number to manufacture**	*Time required in hours*		*Total Time Required*		**Profit per unit**	Total Profit per Article
3				**Cutting**	**Stitching**	**Cutting**	**Stitching**		
4		Shirt	4	1	3	4	12	$ 10.00	$ 40.00
5		Blouse	4	2	2	8	8	$ 12.00	$ 48.00
6			Number of workers	2	3				
7			Hours per day per worker	10	10			Total Profit ->	$ 88.00
8			Work Hours / day	20	30		*Function to Maximize*		
9									
10				Total Time per Process ->		12	20		
11						<=	<=		
12				Constraints ->		20	30		

Figure 3.17: *Calculations when we set to manufacture four shirts and four blouses per day*

We can see that all the constraints are met here. Both and are greater than or equal to 0. The total hours required for cutting is 12, which is less than or equal to 20. The total hours required for stitching is 20, which is less than 30. So, this solution is in the feasible solution area. However, is the profit generated (i.e., $88) the maximum that can be made?

Figure 3.18 shows the calculations when we set to manufacture 10 shirts and 10 blouses per day:

	Article	Number to manufacture	Time required in hours		Total Time Required		Profit per unit	Total Profit per Article
			Cutting	Stitching	Cutting	Stitching		
Shirt		10	1	3	10	30	$ 10.00	$ 100.00
Blouse		10	2	2	20	20	$ 12.00	$ 120.00
	Number of workers		2	3				
	Hours per day per worker		10	10			Total Profit -> $	220.00
	Work Hours / day		20	30			*Function to Maximize*	
		Total Time per Process ->			30	50		
					<=	<=		
		Constraints ->			20	30		

Figure 3.18: Calculations when we set to manufacture 10 shirts and 10 blouses per day

Here, we can see that all the constraints are not met. Both and are greater or equal to 0. The total hours required for cutting is 30, which is not less than or equal to 20. The total hours required for stitching is 50, which is not less than or equal to 30. So, this solution is not in the feasible solution area.

Setting up Solver for the LPP

Now, let's set up Solver to obtain the optimized solution. We need to invoke Solver to do this. Click on the **Data** tab and then on the **Solver**, as shown in *figure 3.19*:

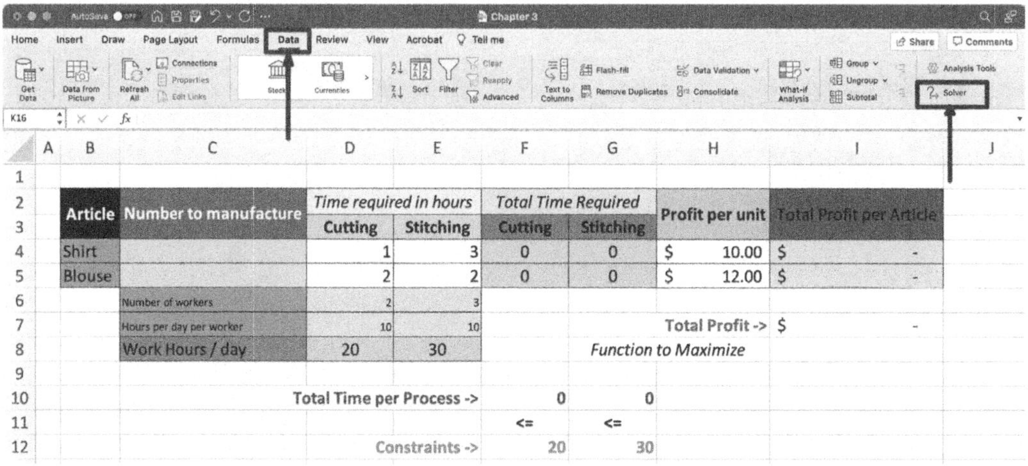

Figure 3.19: Guide to invoking the Solver

The following pop-up is displayed after clicking on the **Solver**:

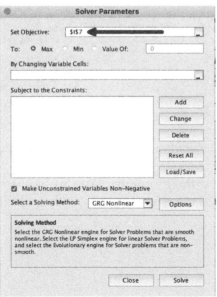

Figure 3.20: *Solver pop-up*

We must set the parameters of the LPP now.

We know that the objective function is to maximize the profit. The total profit is in cell I7, so we will set the objective function to cell I7 in the Solver parameters, as shown in *figure 3.21*:

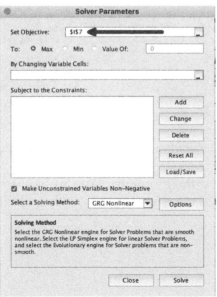

Figure 3.21: *Setting the Objective Function in Solver*

Next, we will set the Solver to state that the problem is for maximizing the objective function, as shown in *figure 3.22*:

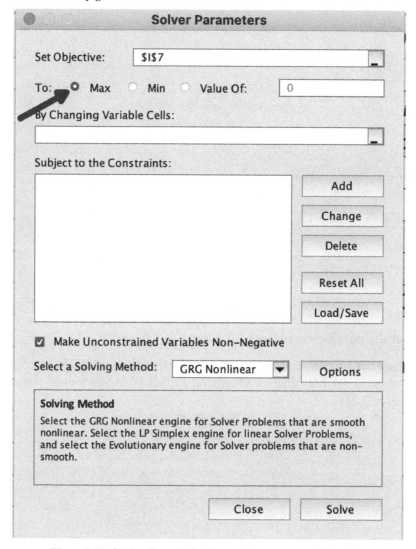

Figure 3.22: Setting the optimization requirement to maximization

We can see that there are three options. We can look to maximize the objective function, minimize the objective function, or set the objective function to a specific value.

Next, we need to set the variables that we want the values for. In our case, the variables are the number of shirts and blouses to manufacture. From *figure 3.15*, we can see that these two variables are set at cells C4 and C5, so we will set these cells as the variables to vary, as shown in *figure 3.23*:

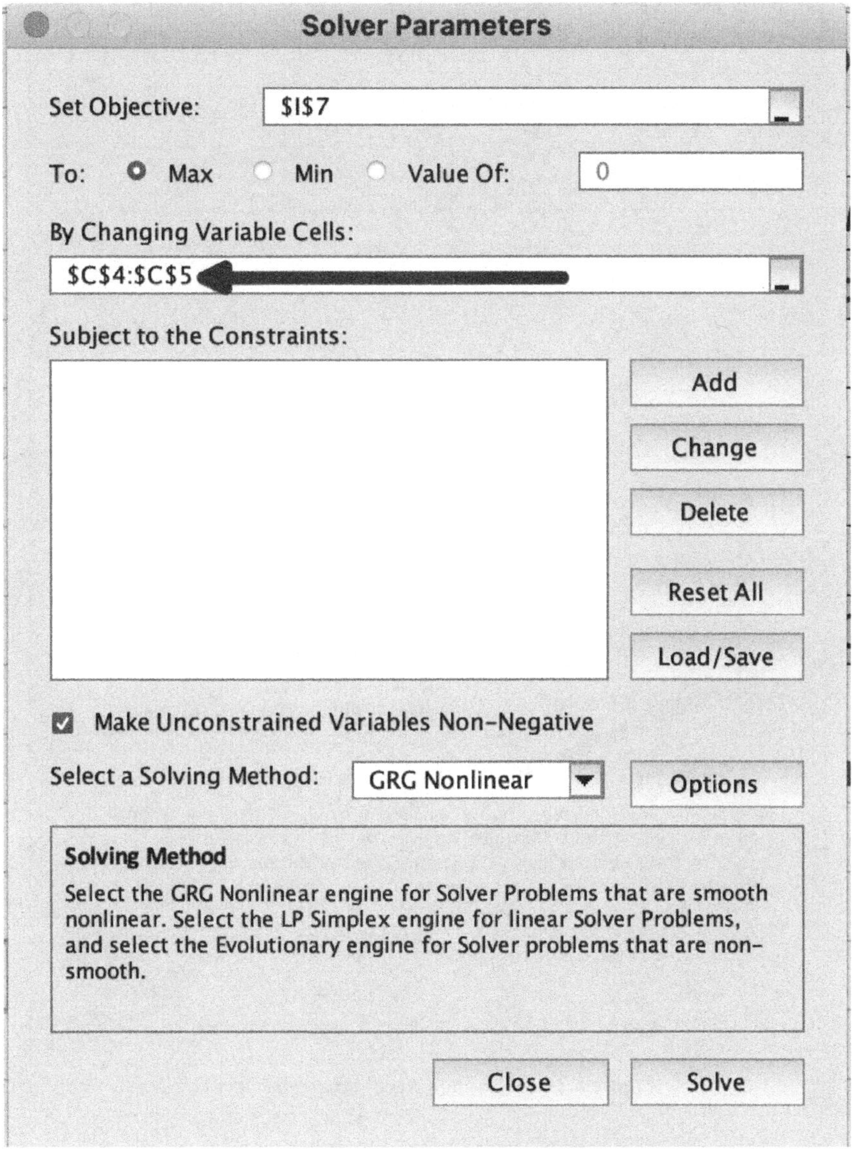

Figure 3.23: Setting the variables to vary to solve the LPP

Next, we need to set the constraints. We have four constraints, two of which are that the and variables must be positive or zero. So, we will check non-negativity needed, as shown in figure 3.24:

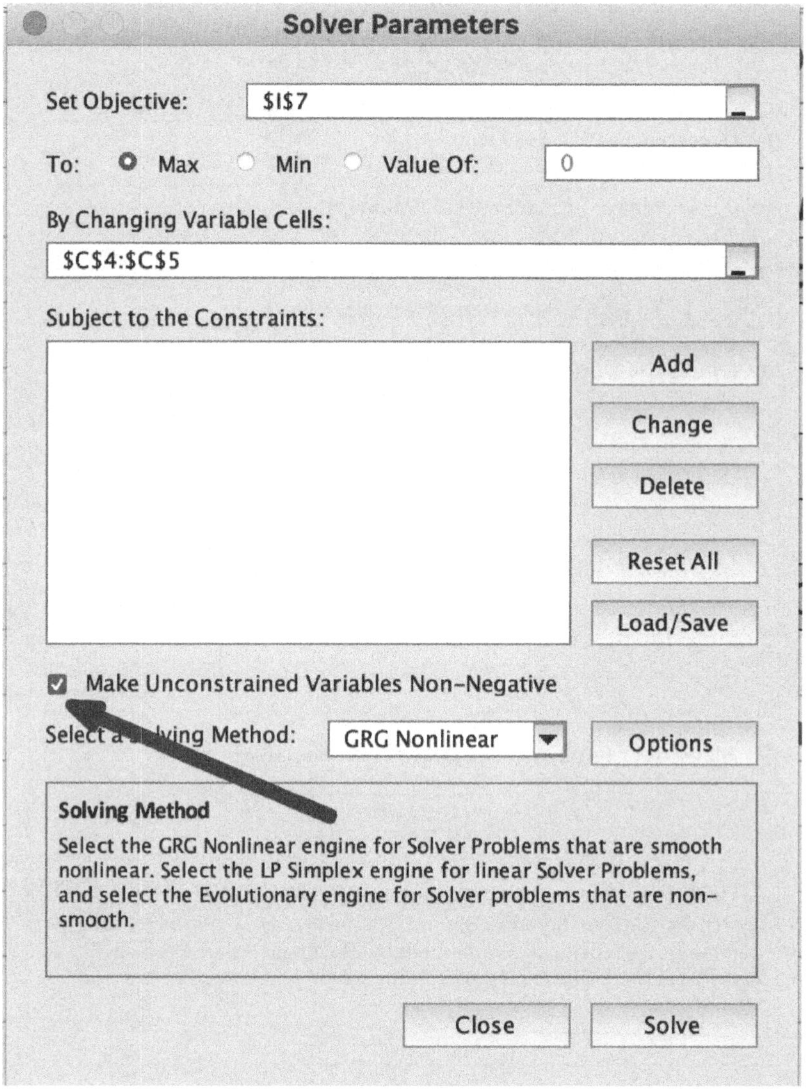

Figure 3.24: *Set the non-negativity requirement*

We will now set the remaining two constraints, which are that the number of hours for cutting and stitching should be less than or equal to an upper limit. We have calculated the total number of hours needed for cutting and stitching in cells F10 and G10, respectively. And we have the upper limits for the hours available for cutting and stitching in cells F12 and G12, respectively.

Click on the **Add** button to add a constraint, as shown in *figure 3.25*:

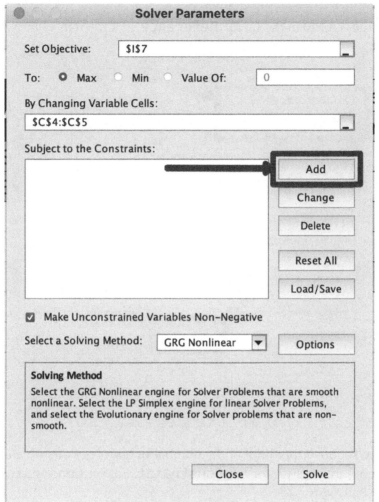

Figure 3.25: *Button to add constraints*

We will get a pop-up on clicking the **Add** button, as shown in *figure 3.26*:

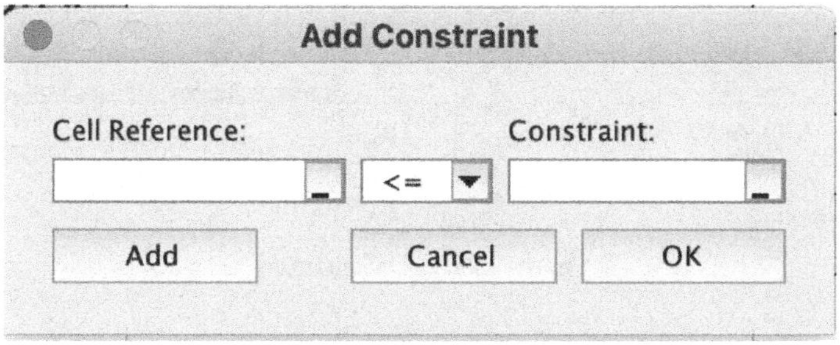

Figure 3.26: *Add Constraint pop-up*

Perform the following steps to add the constraint that the total time for cutting should be less than or equal to 20 hours:

1. Provide cell F10 in the **Cell Reference**, as shown in *figure 3.27*:

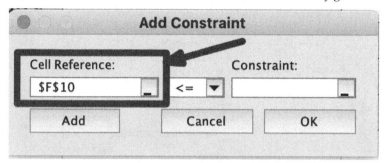

Figure 3.27: Add Cell Reference

2. Set the logical operator to **<=**, as shown in *figure 3.28*:

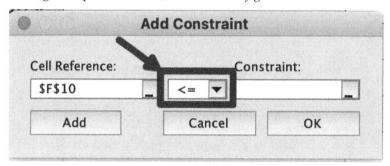

Figure 3.28: Add the logical operator

3. Lastly, set the upper limit of the number of hours per day for cutting, which is stored in cell F12, for the **Constraint**. So, set **Constraint** to F12, as shown in *figure 3.29*:

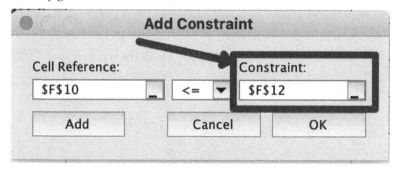

Figure 3.29: Add Constraint

4. Now that the constraint has been defined, click on **OK**, as shown in *figure 3.30*:

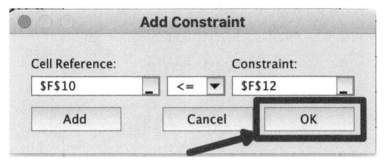

Figure 3.30: *Click on OK to add the constraint*

After adding a constraint, the Solver Parameters pop-up looks as shown in *figure 3.31*:

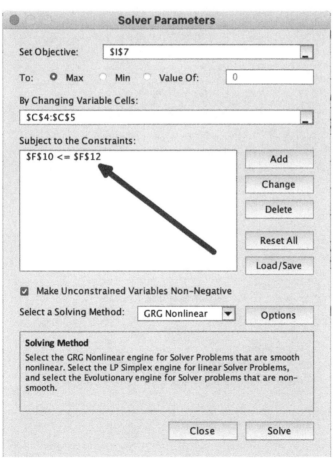

Figure 3.31: *Solver Parameters pop-up after adding a constraint*

Now that we know how to add a constraint, let's add the second constraint in our LPP. We need to add a constraint that the total hours for stitching should be less than or equal to 30 hours per day.

The pop-up will look as follows when we add the constraint:

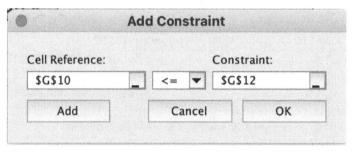

Figure 3.32: *Second constraint defined*

After clicking on **OK**, we will get the **Solver Parameters** as shown in *figure 3.33*:

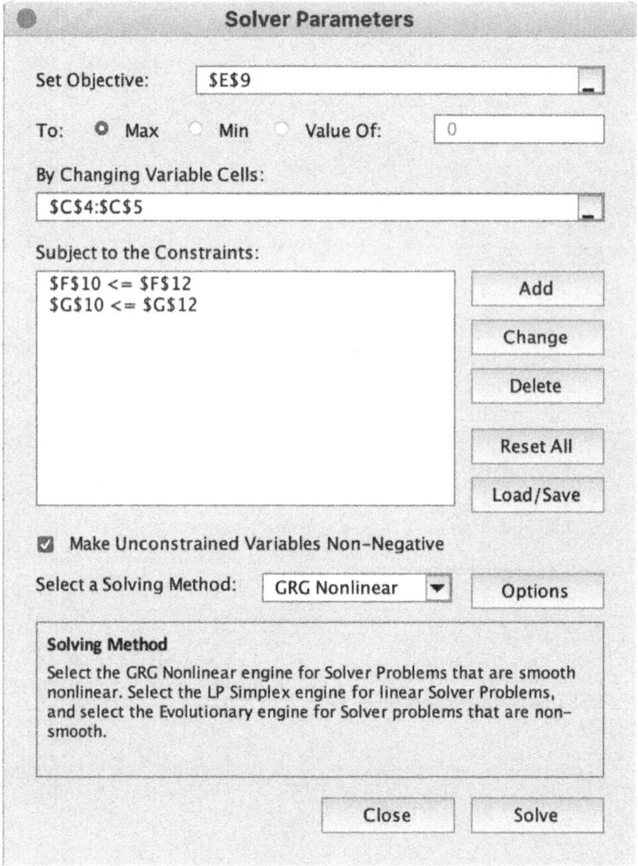

Solver Parameters

Set Objective: $E$9

To: ● Max   ○ Min   ○ Value Of: 0

By Changing Variable Cells:
$C$4:$C$5

Subject to the Constraints:

$F$10 <= $F$12
$G$10 <= $G$12

Add
Change
Delete
Reset All
Load/Save

☑ Make Unconstrained Variables Non-Negative

Select a Solving Method: GRG Nonlinear ▼   Options

Solving Method

Select the GRG Nonlinear engine for Solver Problems that are smooth nonlinear. Select the LP Simplex engine for linear Solver Problems, and select the Evolutionary engine for Solver problems that are non-smooth.

Close   Solve

Figure 3.33: *LPP defined*

We need to set the **Solving Method** before we can ask Solver to solve the LPP. Solver provides 3 solving methods: **Generalized Reduced Gradient** (**GRG**) Nonlinear, Simplex LP, and Evolutionary. It is beyond the scope of this book to discuss the details of the solving methods and the mathematics involved. For our purpose, we should consider the Simplex LP method for most of our requirements as we are discussing linear programming problems. So, we will set the **Solving Method** to **Simplex LP**, as shown in *figure 3.34*:

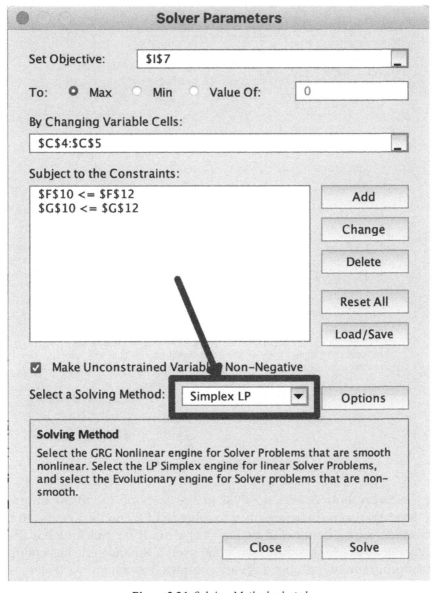

Figure 3.34: *Solving Method selected*

All the necessary **Solver Parameters** have been set up at this stage, so we can click on the **Solve** button, as shown in *figure 3.35*:

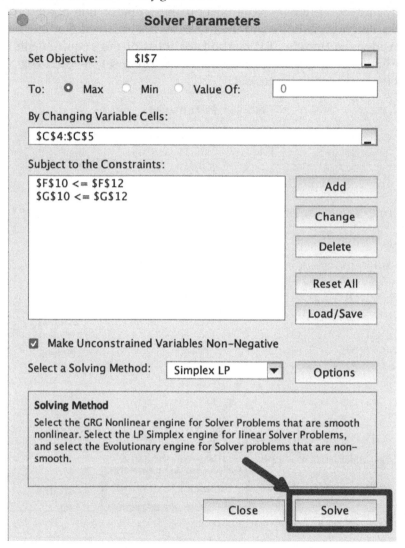

Figure 3.35: *Solve Button to obtain solution from Solver for the LPP*

Clicking the **Solve** button causes Solver to start solving the linear programming problem. It can take some time for Solver to solve an LPP, and the time taken depends on the machine configuration. Solver may not work if the machine has less RAM. Solver may not be able to produce a solution even if the machine has enough RAM if the linear programming problem is very complex (has a lot of variables and many constraints).

The screen looks like this once Solver finishes solving the problem:

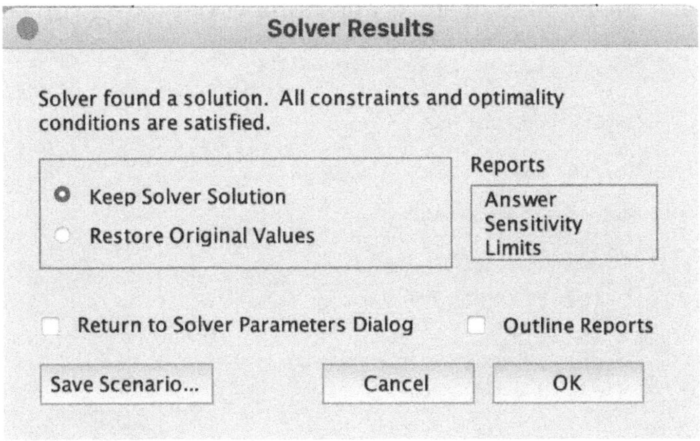

***Figure 3.36**: Intimation from Solving once it has finished solving the LPP*

Click on **OK** to see the solution, as shown in *figure 3.37*:

	A	B	C	D	E	F	G	H	I
1									
2		Article	Number to manufacture	*Time required in hours*		*Total Time Required*		Profit per unit	Total Profit per Article
3				Cutting	Stitching	Cutting	Stitching		
4		Shirt	5	1	3	5	15	$ 10.00	$ 50.00
5		Blouse	7.5	2	2	15	15	$ 12.00	$ 90.00
6			Number of workers	2	3				
7			Hours per day per worker	10	10			Total Profit ->	$ 140.00
8			Work Hours / day	20	30		*Function to Maximize*		
9									
10					Total Time per Process ->	20	30		
11						<=	<=		
12					Constraints ->	20	30		

***Figure 3.37**: Solution provided by Solver*

We can see that the solution states that we need to manufacture 5 shirts and 7.5 blouses per day to maximize profits. However, we know that we cannot manufacture shirts and blouses in fractions, so we can add two more constraints to state that and need to be integers, as shown in *figure 3.38*:

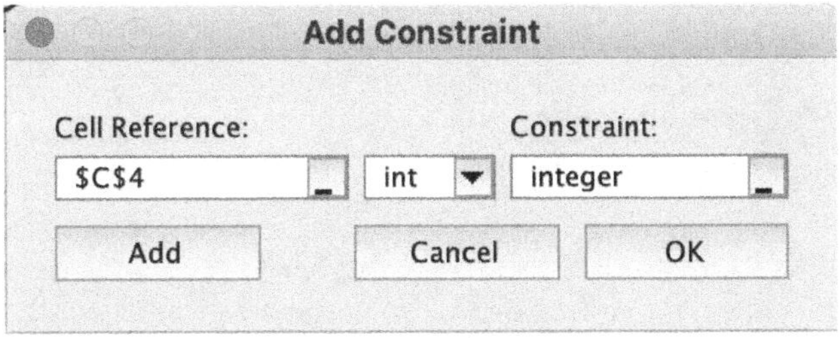

***Figure 3.38**: Constraint set so that the number of shirts is an integer*

The **Solver Parameters** looks as shown in *figure 3.39* on adding these two constraints so that the number of shirts and number of blouses can be integer only:

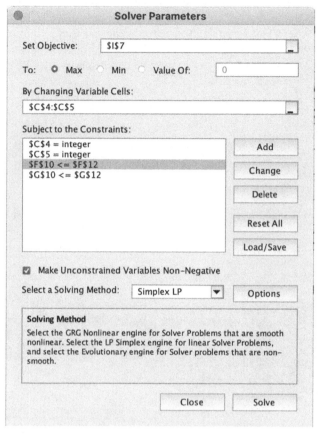

Figure 3.39: *Solver Parameters set so that the number of shirts and blouses to manufacture can be integers only*

On clicking the **Solve** button, we get the result as illustrated in *figure 3.40*:

	Article	Number to manufacture	Time required in hours		Total Time Required		Profit per unit	Total Profit per Article
			Cutting	Stitching	Cutting	Stitching		
Shirt		5	1	3	5	15	$ 10.00	$ 50.00
Blouse		7	2	2	14	14	$ 12.00	$ 84.00
	Number of workers		2	3				
	Hours per day per worker		10	10			Total Profit ->	$ 134.00
	Work Hours / day		20	30		Function to Maximize		
		Total Time per Process ->		19	29			
				<=	<=			
		Constraints ->		20	30			

Figure 3.40: *Solution for Solver Parameters shown in Figure 3.39*

Bill printing problem

We used a simple problem to understand linear programming problems and how to use Solver to solve linear programming problems. Now, let's consider a bigger problem. We will take the example from a telecom company that generates bills for its customers every month. This example can be applied to any company that issues bills to its customers, like credit card companies (banks), water supply companies, electricity providers, and insurance companies.

Let's understand the business side of the problem. A telecom company generally has millions of customers. Every month, the telecom company needs to generate bills, which are sent to the customers by post so that they can make the payment. Generally, the hard copies of the bills must be sent to the customers (Only recently, many telecom companies send the bills by email. However, hard copies of the telecom bills can be used for government requirements for proof of address in many countries. So, many customers request for hard copies of the telephone bills).

Telecom companies have millions of customers, so they divide them into logical units. There are many ways to logically divide the customers. One of the simplest methods is to consider the customers of every district as a logical unit. In telecom company jargon, these districts are called bill cities. Another method used by telecom companies is that they provide the customer with an option for the date when they would like to receive their bills. Based on the date requested by the customers, telecom companies can divide the customers into a maximum of 28 groups (every month is guaranteed to have 28 days).

Telecom companies have specialized machines for printing the bills. Like any others, these machines have a stated speed of printing the bills. Companies generally have more than one such machine to print all the bills for a month within a reasonable time. Now, all the bills for a particular group (whether grouped by bill city or any other grouping) must be printed from a single machine. This is because the bills must be franked after printing before they are dispatched to the customers.

From this basic understanding of the process, let's formulate our problem. Let's consider that a telecom company has 30,00,000 (30 lakhs or 3 million) subscribers. Suppose the telecom company prints all the 3 million bills in one bill printing cycle. Consider that the telecom company has four bill printing machines to print these bills. Each of these machines has the capacity shown in *table 3.1*:

Machine	Bills printed per hour
A	6,400
B	7,000
C	6,800
D	5,500

Table 3.1: Bill printing speeds of the machines

Let's say that the telecom company has divided the customers by bill cities and that it maintains 10 bill cities. The number of subscribers per bill city is as provided in *table 3.2*:

Bill city	Number of subscribers
B1	1,00,000
B2	2,00,000
B3	2,50,000
B4	2,75,000
B5	1,00,000
B6	4,50,000
B7	1,25,000
B8	6,00,000
B9	5,00,000
B10	4,00,000
TOTAL	30,00,000

Table 3.2: Distribution of subscribers in the different bill cities

Lastly, we will consider that we have the constraint of having to complete printing all the bills in 5 days. So, we have a maximum of (5 days * 24 hours/day =) 120 hours per machine to print all the bills.

Let's plant the problem on Microsoft Excel, as shown in *figure 3.41*:

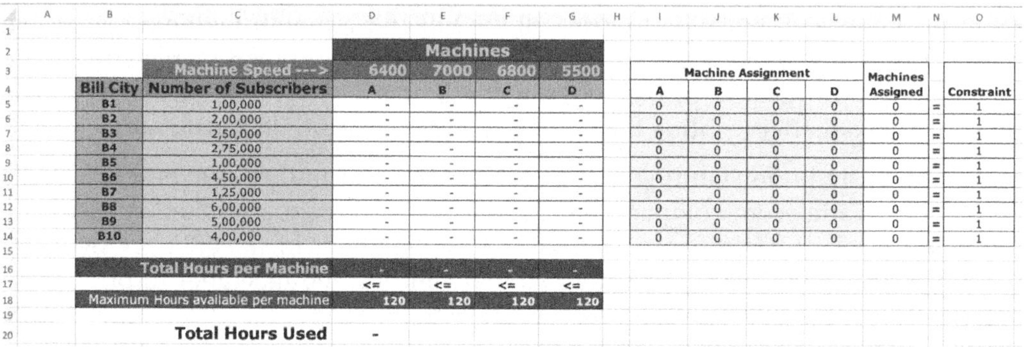

Figure 3.41: Bill printing problem planted on Microsoft Excel

Let's look at the static data first. In Microsoft Excel, we have planted the bill cities in cells B5 to B14, the number of subscribers per bill city in cells C5 to C14, and the machine capacities (i.e., the number of bills printed per hour by each machine) in cells D3, E3, F3, and G3.

Now, look at cells I5 to L14. We expect that each of the cells between I5 and L14 can take a value of 0 or 1. This is because we want to find out which machine will be assigned to which bill city. If a machine is assigned to a bill city, then the corresponding machine and bill city will have a value of 1. For example, cell J7 will have a value of 1 if we assign machine B to bill city B3. So, *cells I5 to L14 are the cells we want to vary.*

In cells M5 to M14, we keep a count of the machines assigned to each bill city. So, cell M5 contains the sum of cells I5, J5, K5, and L5. Enter the formulae as shown in *table 3.3* in cells M5 to M14:

Cell	Formula
M5	=SUM(I5:L5)
M6	=SUM(I6:L6)
M7	=SUM(I7:L7)
M8	=SUM(I8:L8)
M9	=SUM(I9:L9)
M10	=SUM(I10:L10)
M11	=SUM(I11:L11)
M12	=SUM(I12:L12)
M13	=SUM(I13:L13)
M14	=SUM(I14:L14)

Table 3.3: *Formulae to set in cells M5 to M14*

Tip: You can enter the formulae as shown in *table 3.3* in cell M5 and copy this formula to cells M6 to M14.

We know that all the bills for a bill city should be printed by one machine, so the values in cells M5 to M14 should be 1. We will set this constraint in cells O5 to O14 by entering 1 in the cells.

Now, the speed of printing bills for all the machines is mentioned in cells D4, E4, F4, and G4. And the number of bills to print is present in cells C5 to C14. So, we can calculate the number of hours required to print the bills for a bill city by dividing the number of subscribers by the speed of the machine. However, a machine will print bills for a bill city only if it is assigned to a bill city. If machine A is assigned to bill city B1, the number of hours to print all the bills for bill city B1 will be (1,00,000 bills / (6,400 bills / hour) * 1 =) 15.63 hours. So, we can put the formula in cell D5 as C5 / D3 * I5. Enter the following formulae in cells D5 to G14:

Cell	Formula	Cell	Formula		Formula	Cell	Formula
D5	=C5/D3*I5	E5	=C5/E3*J5	F5	=C5/F3*K5	G5	=C5/G3*L5
D6	=C6/D3*I6	E6	=C6/E3*J6	F6	=C6/F3*K6	G6	=C6/G3*L6
D7	=C7/D3*I7	E7	=C7/E3*J7	F7	=C7/F3*K7	G7	=C7/G3*L7
D8	=C8/D3*I8	E8	=C8/E3*J8	F8	=C8/F3*K8	G8	=C8/G3*L8
D9	=C9/D3*I9	E9	=C9/E3*J9	F9	=C9/F3*K9	G9	=C9/G3*L9
D10	=C10/D3*I10	E10	=C10/E3*J10	F10	=C10/F3*K10	G10	=C10/G3*L10
D11	=C11/D3*I11	E11	=C11/E3*J11	F11	=C11/F3*K11	G11	=C11/G3*L11
D12	=C12/D3*I12	E12	=C12/E3*J12	F12	=C12/F3*K12	G12	=C12/G3*L12
D13	=C13/D3*I13	E13	=C13/E3*J13	F13	=C13/F3*K13	G13	=C13/G3*L13
D14	=C14/D3*I14	E14	=C14/E3*J14	F14	=C14/F3*K14	G14	=C14/G3*L14

Table 3.4: Formulae to set in cells D5 to G14

Tip: You can enter the formula =$C5/D$3*I5 in cell D5 and copy it to cells D5 to G14.

Now, we can determine the total number of hours each machine runs for by adding all the assigned hours for the machines. So, we can add the values in cells D5 to D14 to find the total number of hours machine A runs for. So, enter the formulae in *table 3.5* in cells D16, E16, F16, and G16 to calculate the total number of hours spent on each machine:

Cell	Formula
D16	=SUM(D5:D14)
E16	=SUM(E5:E14)
F16	=SUM(F5:F14)
G16	=SUM(G5:G14)

Table 3.5: Formulae to set in cells D16, E16, F16, and G16

Tip: You can enter the formula =SUM(D5:D14) in cell D16 and copy it to cells E16, F16, and G16.

Now, the total number of hours available to each machine is 120, so enter 120 in cells D18, E18, F18, and G18. The values in cells D16, E16, F16, and G16 should be less than the values in cells D18, E18, F18, and G18, respectively.

Note: We will put the same values in cells D18, E18, F18, and G18 because it gives us the flexibility that we can vary the total number of hours available from each machine to a specific value as well. For example, if maximum hours for machine 1 was 100, we could change the value in the cell D18 to 100.
We did the same exercise with cells O5 to O14.

We need to compute the total number of hours consumed by all the machines as this is the value we want to minimize. Enter the formula =SUM(D16:G16) in cell D20:

Cell	Formula
D20	=SUM(D16:G16)

***Table 3.6**: Formula for cell D20*

Cell D20 contains our objective function, which we must minimize.

Let's make an arbitrary assignment of machines to bill cities and see what we get. The setting and output are shown in *figure 3.42*:

		Machines				Machine Assignment						
	Machine Speed --->	6400	7000	6800	5500							
Bill City	Number of Subscribers	A	B	C	D	A	B	C	D	Machines Assigned		Constraint
B1	1,00,000	15.63	-	-	-	1	0	0	0	1	=	1
B2	2,00,000	-	28.57	-	-	0	1	0	0	1	=	1
B3	2,50,000	-	-	36.76	-	0	0	1	0	1	=	1
B4	2,75,000	-	-	-	50.00	0	0	0	1	1	=	1
B5	1,00,000	-	-	14.71	-	0	0	1	0	1	=	1
B6	4,50,000	-	64.29	-	-	0	1	0	0	1	=	1
B7	1,25,000	19.53	-	-	-	1	0	0	0	1	=	1
B8	6,00,000	-	85.71	-	-	0	1	0	0	1	=	1
B9	5,00,000	-	-	73.53	-	0	0	1	0	1	=	1
B10	4,00,000	-	-	-	72.73	0	0	0	1	1	=	1
	Total Hours per Machine	35.16	178.57	125.00	122.73							
		<=	<=	<=	<=							
	Maximum Hours available per machine	120	120	120	120							
	Total Hours Used	461.45										

***Figure 3.42**: Arbitrarily assigning machines to bill cities*

You can see that we assign machine A to bill cities B1 and B7. Similarly, you can see the other machines assigned to the other bill cities. You can see that all the bill cities are assigned exactly one machine, but having made this assignment, we can see that machine A is underutilized and machines B, C, and D have more load than these machines can handle. So, all the constraints are not satisfied by this assignment. We need a solution where all the constraints are met, and the total time taken to print all the bills is the minimum. For this, we need to use Solver to solve this linear programming problem.

We have all the components to set up Solver. There are lots of Solver parameters to set up, so let's state them:

Set **Objective function** to cell *D20*

Set **To** to *Min*

Set **By Changing Variable Cells** to *I5:L14*

Set **Solving Method** to *Simplex LP*

Set the following **constraints**

The constraints stated in *table 3.7* define that all the values of cells I5 to L14 can be either 0 or 1. This is because we want to model so that if a machine is assigned to a bill city, it should have a value of 1, otherwise 0.

Constraints for the LPP			
I5 = binary	J5 = binary	K5 = binary	L5 = binary
I6 = binary	J6 = binary	K6 = binary	L6 = binary
I7 = binary	J7 = binary	K7 = binary	L7 = binary
I8 = binary	J8 = binary	K8 = binary	L8 = binary
I9 = binary	J9 = binary	K9 = binary	L9 = binary
I10 = binary	J10 = binary	K10 = binary	L10 = binary
I11 = binary	J11 = binary	K11 = binary	L11 = binary
I12 = binary	J12 = binary	K12 = binary	L12 = binary
I13 = binary	J13 = binary	K13 = binary	L13 = binary
I14 = binary	J14 = binary	K14 = binary	L14 = binary

Table 3.7: Setting variables to vary to binary constraint

The constraints in *table 3.8* define that we can assign exactly one machine for every bill city:

Constraints for the LPP
M5 = O5
M6 = O6
M7 = O7
M8 = O8
M9 = O9
M10 = O10
M11 = O11
M12 = O12
M13 = O13
M14 = O14

Table 3.8: Constraints to define that every bill city can be assigned exactly one machine

The constraints in *table 3.9* define that every machine should work less than or equal to an upper limit of hours:

Constraints for the LPP
D16 <= D18
E16 <= E18
F16 <= F18
G16 <= G18

***Table 3.9**: Constraints to define that every machine can work less than or equal to an upper limit of hours*

Having made all the discussed set up, solve the linear programming problem. *Figure 3.43* illustrates the obtained result:

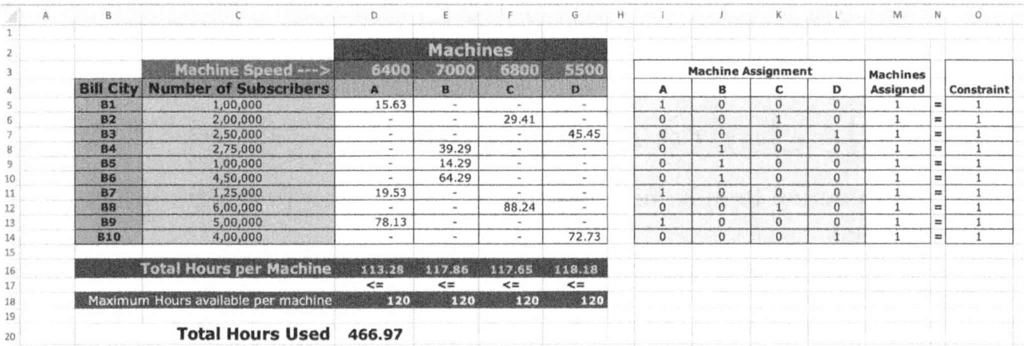

		Machines			
	Machine Speed --->	6400	7000	6800	5500
Bill City	Number of Subscribers	A	B	C	D
B1	1,00,000	15.63	-	-	-
B2	2,00,000	-	-	29.41	-
B3	2,50,000	-	-	-	45.45
B4	2,75,000	-	39.29	-	-
B5	1,00,000	-	14.29	-	-
B6	4,50,000	-	64.29	-	-
B7	1,25,000	19.53	-	-	-
B8	6,00,000	-	-	88.24	-
B9	5,00,000	78.13	-	-	-
B10	4,00,000	-	-	-	72.73
	Total Hours per Machine	113.28	117.86	117.65	118.18
		<=	<=	<=	<=
	Maximum Hours available per machine	120	120	120	120
	Total Hours Used	466.97			

Machine Assignment				Machines Assigned		Constraint
A	B	C	D			
1	0	0	0	1	=	1
0	0	1	0	1	=	1
0	0	0	1	1	=	1
0	1	0	0	1	=	1
0	1	0	0	1	=	1
0	1	0	0	1	=	1
1	0	0	0	1	=	1
0	0	1	0	1	=	1
1	0	0	0	1	=	1
0	0	0	1	1	=	1

***Figure 3.43**: Solution for the linear programming problem*

You can see that all the constraints have been satisfied, and each bill city has been assigned one machine.

Conclusion

Optimization problems exist in all aspects of life and work, but solving problems for the optimal solution is not always simple and intuitive. As a result, we generally tend to depend on our experience to make decisions. That said, the approach of making decisions based on experience and intuition deprives us from making an optimal decision and reduces the benefits.

Optimization problems can be easily solved using a basic computer tool like Microsoft Excel if formulated as linear programming problems. Both simple and complex linear programming problems can be solved using Microsoft Excel.

With this study on linear programming problems, we have covered all the components we need to look at optimally crashing projects based on time and cost.

In the next chapter, we will discuss what is crashing a project and how to crash a project.

Points to remember

- Optimization problems can be modeled as linear programming problems
- Optimization problems take the form where we must either maximize or minimize a quantity
- The quantity to optimize is formulated as the objective function
- The objective function is subject to constraints
- The optimization is conducted by varying a set of variables
- The Solver add-in of Microsoft Excel can be used to solve linear programming problems

Multiple choice questions

1. **The function to maximize or minimize in a linear programming problem is called:**
   a. Optimization function
   b. Maximization function
   c. Objective function
   d. Minimization function

2. **The constraints in a linear programming problem can be:**
   a. Inequalities
   b. Equalities
   c. Both inequalities and equalities
   d. None of the above

3. **Linear programming problems will:**
   a. Always have a solution
   b. Never have a solution
   c. May or may not have a solution
   d. None of the above

4. **When the variable to vary can take a value of 0 or 1, we must:**

   a. Add a constraint so that the variable to vary should be binary

   b. Add a constraint so that the variable to vary should be integer

   c. Add a constraint so that the variable to vary should be positive

   d. None of the above

5. **The objective function can be optimized to:**

   a. Maximize

   b. Minimize

   c. Set to a certain value

   d. Either of the above

Answers

1. c
2. c
3. c
4. a
5. d

Questions

1. ABC Corporation wants to invest $300,000 per week in advertisements. It finds out that advertisements in daytime TV programs cost $5,000 per advertisement. The cost goes up to $7,000 per advertisement during the evening news and $100,000 per advertisement during IPL cricket matches. The reach provided by advertisements during daytime TV programs is 3,000, and this increases to 4,000 during the evening news and 75,000 during IPL matches. ABC Corporation would like to place a minimum of five advertisements per weekday, and it would like to place advertisements in IPL games only on Sundays. Also, ABC Corporation would like to spend a maximum of $50,000 for advertisements on Fridays and a maximum of $75,000 for advertisements on Saturdays. Given ABC Corporation's requirements, what should be the allocation of funds for the different advertisements per weekday.

   (**Hint:** Maximize the reach)

Key terms

- **RAM**: Random Access Memory
- **LPP**: Linear Programming Problem

CHAPTER 4

Crashing a Project

In *section I* of this book, we discussed the components we require to crash a project. We discussed how to set up the project schedule, how to set up the project for monitoring its cost, and how to set up linear programming problems. In this chapter, we will discuss how to use these components to crash a project.

What is meant by *"crashing a project"*? When we reduce a project's timeline, we say that we are crashing the project. In this chapter, we will discuss when we need to crash a project. Then, we will go through the theoretical process of crashing a project and discuss the implications of crashing a project.

Structure

We will discuss the following topics in this chapter:

- The need for crashing a project
- Crash cost
- Crash slope
- Maximum crash duration
- Mechanism for crashing a project
    - ○ Crashing the project by 1 unit duration

     o   Further crashing the project

     o   Plotting the crash cost

Objectives

After studying this chapter, you should be able to understand the concept of crashing a project.

Need for crashing a project

To crash a project means to reduce the time allocated to the project. In other words, we want to complete the project in less time as compared to the time allocated to the project. Reducing the duration of a project is required in many circumstances, some of which are normal and some are forced on the project manager.

We crash a project in two phases of the project. The first case is when a project starts. In most cases, when a project starts, the customer for the project, the management of the project supplier, or both want the project completed earlier than what would have been proposed. Although the vendor would have provided a project plan in the bid document, the customer, in most cases, would want the project to be fast tracked and completed earlier than what would have been mentioned in the RFP. Normally, after the project has been conceived, the customer would spend a decent amount of time to award it to a vendor. This is important for the customer to ensure that the right vendor is selected. However, after the vendor has been selected, the customer would want to make up for the lost time. So, in the kickoff meeting of the project, the sponsor of the project would want to see innovation from the vendor to reduce the time to deliver the project. There are other motivations for the customer like some competitor would be working on a similar product. Though it may seem unjustified to the project team, they should always be prepared for this. One of the ways to mitigate this risk is to build some buffers in the proposed project plan submitted in the bid. This strategy has risks as it may increase the proposed project duration and score negatively against the vendor during the selection process.

Also, when a project is won, the management of the company that awarded the project generally asks the project team to provide the least time in which the project could be completed. In other words, they would want a project plan that completes the project in less time than what was proposed in the bid. Such a demand has three primary motivations. The first is that the vendor would like to complete the project before time and score brownie points from the customer. Another motivation is that the vendor would like to complete the project as early as possible, realize the money, and showcase the project to other customers to gain more business. A third motivation with many managers is that they would like to keep a time cushion with themselves so that the project has the least amount of schedule overrun in worse circumstances.

The second case when a project needs crashing is when it is in execution. Almost all projects come across situations where they may be running behind schedule. Generally, projects do not run behind schedule because of the project team or the project manager's inefficiency but because of unexpected issues that arise when a project is in execution. There can be many instances of where the customer demands extra features or changes the originally stated requirements. Technical assumptions often prove to be wrong, and new techniques must be devised. There can be manpower turnover in a project, and the necessary equipment and other resources may be supplied late to the project. When a project is running behind schedule, the management and the project manager make an effort to bring it back on track. The project needs to be crashed to do so.

In summary, it is prudent to say that crashing a project is almost an inherent requirement of a project.

Crash cost

When we crash a project, we usually incur some cost. *This cost involved in crashing a project is called the crash cost.*

Let's understand this through an example. Let's consider a small-scale industry manufacturing garments, and let's say that this company gets an order to deliver 10,000 jackets in 1 month. We will only consider the task of stitching the jackets for our example. Suppose this company has 20 tailors to work on this order, and the company has 20 machines for this project.

We will make a few more assumptions, as follows:

- The company pays Rs.20,000 per month as rent for its manufacturing site
- At an average, the company incurs Rs.5,000 electricity bill per month
- At an average, the company needs Rs.10,000 per month for all other expenses
- The tailors are hired at a rate of Rs.200 per day
- The machines are rented for Rs.2,000 per month
- There are 20 working days in a month
- The tailors work for 8 hours per day, so we will consider the number of productive hours to be 5 hours per day
- Every tailor can manufacture 5 jackets per hour
- Lastly, we consider that the company has no other orders at the time

Let's first check whether it is practical to complete this project in 1 month:

1. 1 tailor can stitch 5 jackets per hour.

2. 1 tailor can stitch (5 jackets/hour * 5 hours/day) = 25 jackets/day.

3. 1 tailor can stitch (25 jackets/day * 20 days/month) = 500 jackets/month.

4. 20 tailors can stitch (500 jackets/month/Tailor * 20 Tailors) = 10,000 jackets/month.

So, we see that the task to stitch 10,000 jackets in a month is feasible under our assumptions.

Now, let's apply cost-based pricing to determine the cost of this task. For pricing purposes, we will consider that the material for manufacturing the jackets has been provided by the customer, so the company does not have to incur the cost.

- Rent for the manufacturing base = Rs.20,000 (the place is needed for a month for this project)

- Expenses toward electricity = Rs.5,000 (The electricity cost for 1 month)

- Other expenses = Rs.10,000 (Other expenses for 1 month)

- Wages for the tailors = Rs.200/day/tailor * 20 days * 20 tailors = Rs.80,000

- Rent for the machines = Rs.2,000/month/machine * 20 machines = Rs.40,000

So, total cost = (Rs.20,000 + Rs.5,000 + Rs.10,000 + Rs.80,000 + Rs.40,000) = Rs. 1,55,000

To complete the project in 1 month as per the plan, we will need Rs.1,55,000.00 (rupees one lakh fifty-five thousand only).

Now, let's say that the management asks for this task of stitching 10,000 jackets to be completed in 10 working days instead of 20. So, we have a situation where we must crash this task. The project manager decides to hire 20 more tailors to complete the work as the number of jackets that one tailor can stitch in an hour cannot be increased any further. Also, let's assume that the working hours cannot be extended, so the project manager decides to rent 20 additional machines.

So, the company needs to hire 20 tailors for 10 days. Normally, the company was paying Rs.200 per tailor per day, but the labor rates are higher for short duration work as this labor would not be retained beyond the duration of engagement. So, let's say that the 20 new tailors are hired at Rs.225 per day per tailor.

The company also needs to rent 20 machines for 10 days. Again, when equipment is rented for a short duration, the rent is normally higher than the regular rent. Let's say the rent of the additional machines is Rs.2,300 per machine per month.

Now, the project would need all the initial cost that we have calculated because the manufacturing site will have to be retained for the entire month, even though this project would be completed in half a month. Similarly, the company would have to pay electricity bills for the entire month. Also, the company must pay the original set of tailors and the rental for the initial set of 20 machines for the entire month. Let's say the other expenses increase from Rs.10,000 to Rs.15,000 from hiring 20 new tailors and renting 20 new machines.

So, the new cost of the task would be as follows:

- Original cost of the project = Rs.1,55,000

- Increase in other expenses = Rs.5,000

- Cost of 20 additional tailors = Rs.225/day/tailor * 10 days * 20 tailors = Rs.45,000

- Cost of 20 additional machines = Rs.2,300/month/machine / 20 days/ month * 10 days * 20 machines = Rs.23,000

So, the cost after crashing the project is (Rs.1,55,000 + Rs.5,000 + Rs.45,000 + Rs.23,000) = Rs.2,28,000 (rupees two lakhs twenty-eight thousand only).

So, we see that the project cost has increased after crashing the project.

Let's say that we don't want to incur the cost of the original set of machines and the original set of tailors for the full month as the project will be completed in half a month. In that case, the calculations would be as follows:

- Original cost of the project = Rs.1,55,000

- Minus the cost of the original tailors for 20 days = Rs.80,000

- Minus the cost of the original machines for 20 days = Rs.40,000

- Cost of the original tailors for 10 days = Rs.40,000

- Cost of the original machines for 10 days = Rs.20,000

- Increase in other expenses = Rs.5,000

- Cost of 20 additional tailors = Rs.225/day/tailor * 10 days * 20 tailors = Rs.45,000

- Cost of 20 additional machines = Rs.2,300/month/machine / 20 days/ month * 10 days * 20 machines = Rs.23,000

Under this calculation, the cost of the project after crashing the project would be (Rs.1,55,000 − Rs.80,000 − Rs.40,000 + Rs.40,000 + Rs.20,000 + Rs.5,000 + Rs.45,000 + Rs.23,000 =) Rs.1,68,000 (rupees one lakh sixty-eight thousand only).

So, we see that the cost is higher than the original task cost in this case as well. This increase in cost is called the **crash cost**. So, in our example, the crash cost is (Rs.168,000 – Rs.1,55,000 =) Rs.13,000 (rupees thirteen thousand only). In other words, the cost of the task of stitching 10,000 jackets increases by Rs.13,000 if the task duration is reduced by 10 working days.

Crash slope

The cost per unit reduction in the project duration is called the crash cost.

Let's understand this through our example. We saw that the cost of reducing the project duration from 20 working days to 10 working days was Rs.13,000. In other words, the crash cost is Rs.13,000 to reduce the project duration by 10 days, so the per day crash cost is (Rs.13,000 / 10 days =) Rs.1,300/day. So, Rs.1,300 is the crash slope in our example.

Maximum crash duration

We reduce the duration of one or more of the tasks in the project when we crash a project. Now, there is a limit to how much the duration of a task can be reduced. *The maximum amount of time by which the duration of a task can be reduced is called the maximum crash duration.*

We did a simple exercise in our example, where we decreased the task duration to half by doubling the number of tailors and machines. However, we will not always find such linear relations when we reduce the duration of tasks. For instance, when we added new tailors in our example, we should have considered that the new tailors may need 2 days of training to understand this project. So, we would effectively get 8 days of work from the new tailors. Under this assumption, the new tailors would produce (5 jackets/hour * 5 hours/day * 8 days =) 200 jackets in 10 days instead of 250 jackets in 10 days. So, we will not be able to complete the project if we engage 20 new tailors for 10 days. The project cannot reduce the duration of this task of stitching 10,000 jackets by 10 days if we can't get more than 20 new tailors.

Consider a case from a software development project. In a software project, we would have a task for load testing. One of the tests in load testing is that we test the system under the peak load that the system is expected to experience. Suppose the system is designed to process the peak load in 3 days, and we must conduct three rounds of load testing. In this case, the minimum duration we would need for load testing is (3 rounds * 3 days/round =) 9 days. Suppose the original amount of time allocated to the task of load testing is 15 days. So, the task of load testing the system in this project can be reduced by a maximum of 6 days as the task needs a minimum of 9 days.

Mechanism for crashing a project

We have established the essential components for crashing a project. Now, we will look at the process of crashing a project. We need a project to do this.

Consider the original plan for a project, as shown in *figure 4.1*:

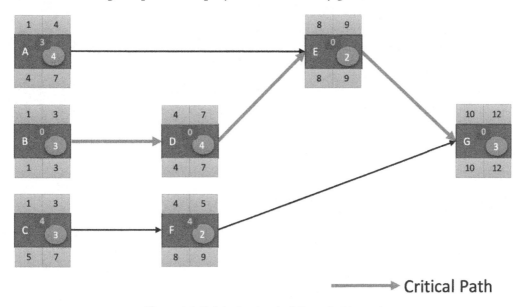

→ Critical Path

Figure 4.1: Original network of the project to crash

We get the following calculation in Excel for the project shown in *figure 4.1*:

	A	B	C	D	E	F	G	H	I	J	K
1	Activity	Description	Duration	Crash Time	Crash Slope	Predecessor	ES	EF	LS	LF	Slack
2	A	Write Instructions	4	1	$ 400.00		1	4	4	7	3
3	B	Select Technique	3	1	$ 350.00		1	3	1	3	0
4	C	Procure Equipment	3	2	$ 375.00		1	3	5	7	4
5	D	Select Operators	4	2	$ 400.00	B	4	7	4	7	0
6	E	Train Operators	2	1	$ 600.00	D,A	8	9	8	9	0
7	F	Install Equipment	2			C	4	5	8	9	4
8	G	Check Procedures	3	1	$ 200.00	F,E	10	12	10	12	0

Figure 4.2: Project schedule from figure 4.1 planted on Excel

In *figure 4.2*, the **Crash Slope** column indicates the cost of reducing the duration of each task by 1 unit. So, the crash cost incurred would be $ 400 if we reduce the duration of task A from 4 units to 3 units. The crash cost incurred would be ($ 400 * 2 =) $ 800 if we reduce the duration of task A by 2 units.

Look at the **Crash Time** column in *figure 4.2*. The values in this column indicate the maximum units of duration by which a task can be crashed. So, we can reduce the duration of task A by 1 unit at most. So, the minimum time required for task A is (4 – 1) = 3 units.

We can now calculate the minimum duration required for each task by subtracting **Crash Time** from **Duration**, as shown in *figure 4.3*:

	A	B	C	D	E	F	G	H	I	J	K	L
1	Activity	Description	Duration	Crash Time	Minimum Duration	Crash Slope	Predecessor	ES	EF	LS	LF	Slack
2	A	Write Instructions	4	1	3	$ 400.00		1	4	4	7	3
3	B	Select Technique	3	1	2	$ 350.00		1	3	1	3	0
4	C	Procure Equipment	3	2	1	$ 375.00		1	3	5	7	4
5	D	Select Operators	4	2	2	$ 400.00	B	4	7	4	7	0
6	E	Train Operators	2	1	1	$ 600.00	D,A	8	9	8	9	0
7	F	Install Equipment	2		2		C	4	5	8	9	4
8	G	Check Procedures	3	1	2	$ 200.00	F,E	10	12	10	12	0

Figure 4.3: Minimum duration required for each task calculated

Crashing the project by 1 unit duration

Now, let's reduce the duration of the project by 1 unit. We need to reduce the duration of one or more tasks to reduce the duration of the project, so we must choose the task whose duration can be reduced.

We know that the longest path in the project schedule is the critical path, so the project duration will reduce if we reduce the duration of the task on the critical path.

So, *the first step is to check the tasks on the critical path whose durations can be reduced.*

In our project schedule (refer to *figure 4.1*), the tasks on the critical path are tasks B, D, E, and G.

From *figure 4.2*, we gather that we can reduce the duration of tasks B, D, E, and G by a minimum of 1 unit.

The next step is to determine the task (on the critical path) which will cost the least if crashed. So, we will calculate the cost of reducing the duration of tasks B, D, E, and G by 1 unit.

Task	Cost of crashing task by 1 unit
B	$ 350
D	$ 400
E	$ 600
G	$ 200

Table 4.1: Cost of crashing tasks on the critical path by 1 unit

From *table 4.1*, we understand that the cost of reducing task G is the least, so we will reduce the duration of task G by 1 unit. We will get the project network as shown in *figure 4.4* after crashing task G by 1 unit:

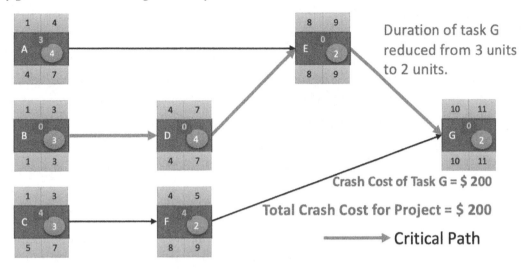

Figure 4.4: Project crashed by 1 unit

We notice the following after crashing the project by 1 unit:

- The crash cost is $ 200.

- The critical path of the project does not change after crashing task G by 1 unit. This may not be the case every time we perform this exercise; this case is specific to our example.

Further crashing the project

Now, let's reduce the duration of the project by 1 more unit. Again, we will consider the tasks on the critical path and crash the task that incurs the least cost.

The tasks on the critical path are B, D, E and G. However, we cannot crash task G any further as task G requires a minimum of 2 units (refer to *figure 4.3*) and it is presently planned to be completed in 2 units (refer to *figure 4.4*). So, we will analyze tasks B, D, and E. The cost of crashing tasks B, D, and E by 1 unit is shown in *table 4.2*:

Task	Cost of crashing task by 1 unit
B	$ 350
D	$ 400
E	$ 600

Table 4.2: Cost of crashing tasks B, D, and E by 1 unit

We can see that we will incur the least cost if we reduce the duration of task B by 1 unit. So, we will crash task B by 1 unit to get the project network as illustrated in *figure 4.5*:

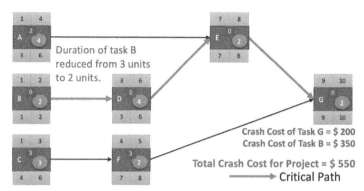

Figure 4.5: *Project further crashed by crashing task B by 1 unit*

We now have a plan to execute the project in 10 units of time as compared to the initial plan of completing the project in 12 units of time. Let's reduce the duration of the project by 1 more unit. The critical path passes through tasks B, D, E, and G, but we cannot crash tasks B and G (refer to *figure 4.3*). So, we must choose from tasks D and E. We can see the cost of crashing tasks D and E by 1 unit in *table 4.3*:

Task	Cost of crashing task by 1 unit
D	$ 400
E	$ 600

Table 4.3: *Cost of crashing tasks D and E by 1 unit*

We see that the cost of crashing task D is lower than that of crashing task E, so we will crash task D by 1 unit to get the project network as shown in *figure 4.6*:

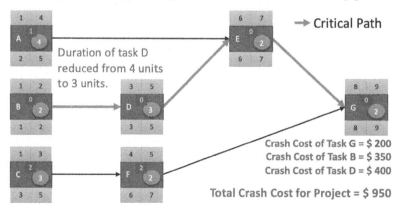

Figure 4.6: *Project further crashed by crashing task D by 1 unit*

As shown in *figure 4.6*, the critical path of the project network has not changed after crashing task D by 1 unit. Further, we can see that we can crash task D by 1 more unit and task E by 1 unit, and both tasks D and E are on the critical path. The cost of crashing task D is less than the cost of crashing task E (refer to *table 4.3*), so we will crash task D by 1 more unit to get the project network as shown in *figure 4.7*:

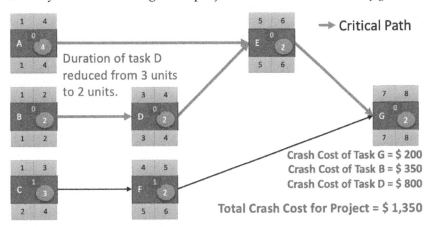

Figure 4.7: Project further crashed by further crashing task D by 1 unit

We can now see that task A is also on the critical path, so we have two critical paths for the project now. This means the project is riskier than before. Also, note that we have incurred a cost of $1,350 in crashing the project from 12 units to 8 units duration.

Let's see if we can crash the project further. Now, we can crash tasks E and A on the critical path. The cost of crashing 1 unit of tasks A and E is as shown in *table 4.4*:

Task	Cost of crashing task by 1 unit
A	$ 400
E	$ 600

Table 4.4: Cost of crashing tasks A and E by 1 unit

Task A has a lower crash cost, so we will crash task A by 1 unit. The project network is as shown in *figure 4.8*:

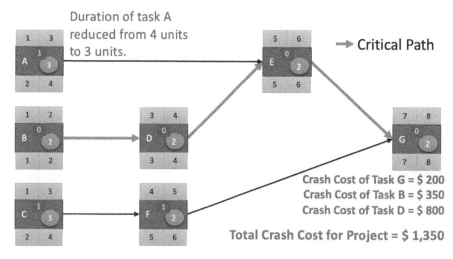

The duration of the project does not reduce. So, we reject this move.

Figure 4.8: Duration of task A crashed by 1 unit

We can see that the project duration does not reduce by reducing the duration of task A, so we will reject this move.

We can now try to reduce the duration of task E and see whether the project duration reduces. We will start from the project network we had as per *figure 4.7* to get the project network as shown in *figure 4.9*:

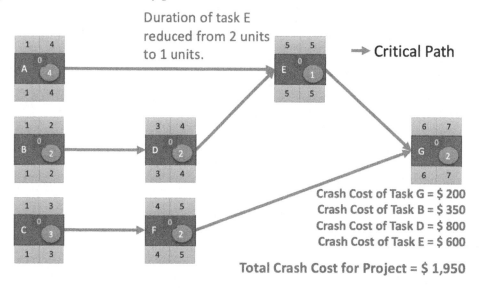

Figure 4.9: Duration of task E crashed by 1 unit

In *figure 4.9*, we can see that all the tasks in the project are now on the critical path. This implies that the project can no longer be crashed. So, this project can be completed in a minimum duration of 7 units.

We crashed the project from 12 units duration to 7 units duration, and the crash cost in doing so is $1,950.

Plotting the crash cost

We noticed that we were incurring a cost at every step of reducing the project duration by 1 unit. Let's plot the crash cost for every unit of reduction. We will get the graphs as shown in *figure 4.10*:

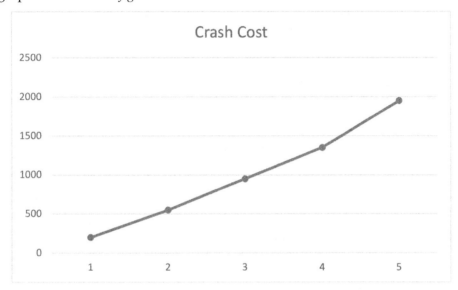

Figure 4.10: *Crash cost per unit of reduction in project duration*

We note that the total crash cost is rising by reducing the project duration by every unit. The project management must decide by how much they would like to crash the project; the cost of crashing the project should not exceed the total benefits from the project.

So, *the project management team should set a target as to what extent the project should be crashed before it can be crashed.*

Conclusion

Project managers mostly face the requirement to complete the project in less time than originally planned, which is called crashing the project. A project may need crashing at the start of the project or when it is in execution.

There is a cost associated with crashing a project, which is called crash cost. This cost is incurred because additional resources in the form of manpower and/or machines and equipment are required when a project is crashed.

We must ensure that we incur the least cost when we crash a project. At every step in the process of crashing a project, we need to evaluate which task will result in maximum reduction in duration at the least cost if crashed. A task in the project will have a limit as to how much it can be crashed.

We saw that crashing a project manually can take an enormous amount of time. In the next chapter, we will set up crashing a project as a linear programming problem and solve it.

Points to remember

- The cost incurred in crashing a project is called the crash cost.

- The crash cost required per unit reduction in project duration is called crash slope.

- There is a limit to how much the duration can be reduced in conducting a task in the project. This limit is called the maximum crash duration for a task.

- Crashing a project is a step-by-step process. At each step of crashing a project, we need to select a task that will result in the least crash cost.

Multiple choice questions

1. **If the cost of crashing a task by 5 units of duration is Rs.20,000, the crash slope is:**

    a. Rs.10,000

    b. Rs.5,000

    c. Rs.4,000

    d. Cannot be determined

2. **A task has been planned for 20 days in the initial project plan and requires a minimum of 12 days to complete. What is the maximum crash duration?**

    a. 20 days

    b. 12 days

    c. 8 days

    d. Cannot be determined

3. While crashing a project, the candidate tasks that can be crashed for a step are A, B, and C. The crash slope of task A is Rs.1,000, task B is Rs.1,100, and task C is Rs.900. Which task should be crashed in this step of crashing the project?

   a. Task A

   b. Task B

   c. Task C

   d. Cannot be determined

4. While crashing a project, the current duration of the project is 22 weeks. Task D is crashed by 1 unit during the step of crashing the project. After this step, the project duration is 22 weeks. What should we do?

   a. Accept the crashing of task D

   b. Discard the crashing of task D

   c. Cannot be determined

Answers

1. c
2. c
3. c
4. b

Questions

1. Crash the project shown in *figure 4.11*. By how many units of duration can this project be crashed? Plot the crash cost at each step of crashing the project.

Activity	Description	Duration	Crash Time	Crash Slope	Predecessor
A	Write Instructions	4	1	$ 400.00	
B	Select Technique	3			
C	Procure Equipment	3	2	$ 375.00	
D	Select Operators	4			B
E	Train Operators	2	1	$ 600.00	D,A
F	Install Equipment	2			C
G	Check Procedures	3			F,E

Figure 4.11: Project schedule for problem 1

2. **Crash the project shown in *figure 4.12*. By how many units of duration can this project be crashed? Plot the crash cost at each step of crashing the project.**

Activity	Duration	Predecessor	Crash Duration	Crash Cost
A	5		2	$ 500.00
B	9	A	3	$ 450.00
C	2	B		
D	3	B	1	$ 600.00
E	17	C,D	5	$ 200.00
F	45	C	10	$ 250.00
H	10	D	2	$ 400.00
J	56	E,R	15	$ 375.00
K	90	F,E	20	$ 350.00
L	32	J,K	4	$ 250.00
R	24	H	6	$ 500.00

Figure 4.12: Project schedule for problem 2

Key terms

- **Crash Cost**: The cost incurred in crashing a project
- **Crash Slope**: Crash cost per unit reduction in project duration

CHAPTER 5

Using LPP to Crash a Project

In the previous chapter, we discussed the mechanism for crashing a project. We saw that the process is quite cumbersome even for a small project. We need a mechanism that allows us to easily crash a project using tools.

One answer to our need is to formulate the problem for crashing a project as a linear programming problem. Once this is done, we can use tools like Microsoft Excel to solve these linear programming problems and obtain solutions for crashing a project. In this chapter, we will discuss how to formulate a problem for crashing a project as a linear programming problem and solve it using Microsoft Excel.

As we saw in *Chapter 3, Linear Programming Problems*, the Solver add-in of Microsoft Excel encapsulates all the complexities involved in solving linear programming problems. A problem for crashing a project formulated as a linear programming problem has a lot of variables and constraints, even if it's a small project. The scale of the problem is gigantic when we use this tool for a large project. In this chapter, we will see that it needs to dexterously formulate the problem and then carefully set up Solver so that we obtain the solution. We must understand the requirements for setting up the linear programming problem for crashing a project using Solver. This is because Solver has its specific mechanism for accepting the inputs so that it can generate a solution. Pay specific attention to how the problem is parameterized so that the same setup can be used for obtaining solutions for different situations.

We will discuss different cases of crashing a project based on time and cost.

Structure

We will discuss the following topics in this chapter:

- Setting up the LPP
- Adding constraint for upper limit of crash cost
- Crashing the project to a stated duration

Objectives

After studying this unit, you should be able to formulate problems for crashing a project using Microsoft Excel and solve them using Microsoft Excel's Solver add-in.

Setting up the LPP

Let's restate the project plan we discussed in the previous chapter. We will set this project plan as a linear programming problem and then solve it for conducting the project in the minimum possible time.

Figure 5.1 illustrates the network diagram for our project:

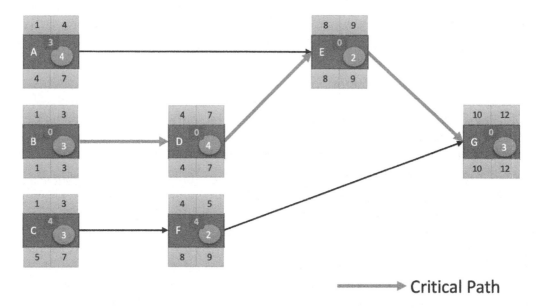

Figure 5.1: Network diagram of project to crash

This project network looks as shown in *figure 5.2* when we formulate it on a Microsoft Excel sheet:

	A	B	C	D	E	F	G	H	I	J	K
1	Activity	Description	Duration	Crash Time	Crash Slope	Predecessor	ES	EF	LS	LF	Slack
2	A	Write Instructions	4	1	$ 400.00		1	4	4	7	3
3	B	Select Technique	3	1	$ 350.00		1	3	1	3	0
4	C	Procure Equipment	3	2	$ 375.00		1	3	5	7	4
5	D	Select Operators	4	2	$ 400.00	B	4	7	4	7	0
6	E	Train Operators	2	1	$ 600.00	D,A	8	9	8	9	0
7	F	Install Equipment	2			C	4	5	8	9	4
8	G	Check Procedures	3	1	$ 200.00	F,E	10	12	10	12	0

Figure 5.2: Project network of figure 5.1 planted on Microsoft Excel

From *figure 5.2*, we can see that the project duration in the current state is 12 units. Note that **Early Start (ES)**, **Early Finish (EF)**, **Late Start (LS)**, and **Late Finish (LF)** are calculated based on the duration in column C of the Microsoft Excel sheet.

We will add two columns to the Microsoft Excel sheet in *figure 5.2* to state the minimum and maximum duration available for a task. We will assume that the maximum duration available for a task is the currently stated duration in column C of the Microsoft Excel sheet. The minimum duration available is the maximum duration available minus the crash time. This is because we have determined that the tasks can be crashed by the amount as stated in the crash time (mentioned in column C of the Microsoft Excel sheet). The updated Microsoft Excel sheet looks like this:

	A	B	C	D	E	F	G	H	I	J	K	L	M
1	Activity	Description	Duration	Crash Time	Minimum Duration	Maximum Duration	Crash Slope	Predecessor	ES	EF	LS	LF	Slack
2	A	Write Instructions	4	1	3	4	$ 400.00		1	4	4	7	3
3	B	Select Technique	3	1	2	3	$ 350.00		1	3	1	3	0
4	C	Procure Equipment	3	2	1	3	$ 375.00		1	3	5	7	4
5	D	Select Operators	4	2	2	4	$ 400.00	B	4	7	4	7	0
6	E	Train Operators	2	1	1	2	$ 600.00	D,A	8	9	8	9	0
7	F	Install Equipment	2		2	2		C	4	5	8	9	4
8	G	Check Procedures	3	1	2	3	$ 200.00	F,E	10	12	10	12	0

Figure 5.3: Columns added for calculating minimum and maximum duration for every task

To calculate the values in columns E and F in *figure 5.3*, insert the following formulae in the cells as stated in *table 5.1*:

Cell	Formula	Cell	Formula
E2	=C2-D2	F2	=C2
E3	=C3-D3	F3	=C3
E4	=C4-D4	F4	=C4
E5	=C5-D5	F5	=C5
E6	=C6-D6	F6	=C6
E7	=C7-D7	F7	=C7
E8	=C8-D8	F8	=C8

Table 5.1: Formulae to be entered for calculating the minimum and maximum task duration

Tip: Enter the formulae stated in *table 5.1* in cells E2 and F2. Copy the cells E2 and F2 and paste the values in cells E3 to F8.

We will add one more column to the Microsoft Excel sheet shown in *figure 5.3*—for **Crashed Duration**. Crashed Duration will be the duration of the task after the project has been crashed, so it will be an integer between the minimum duration and the maximum duration. *Figure 5.4* illustrates the Microsoft Excel sheet after this update:

	A	B	C	D	E	F	G	H	I	J	K	L	M	N
1	Activity	Description	Duration	Crash Time	Minimum Duration	Maximum Duration	Crash Slope	Predecessor	Crashed Duration	ES	EF	LS	LF	Slack
2	A	Write Instructions	4	1	3	4	$ 400.00			1	4	4	7	3
3	B	Select Technique	3	1	2	3	$ 350.00			1	3	1	3	0
4	C	Procure Equipment	3	2	1	3	$ 375.00			1	3	5	7	4
5	D	Select Operators	4	2	2	4	$ 400.00	B		4	7	4	7	0
6	E	Train Operators	2	1	1	2	$ 600.00	D,A		8	9	8	9	0
7	F	Install Equipment	2		2	2		C		4	5	8	9	4
8	G	Check Procedures	3	1	2	3	$ 200.00	F,E		10	12	10	12	0

Figure 5.4: Column added for Crashed Duration

We will initialize **Crashed Duration** to the present values of the **Duration** (as shown in column C of the Microsoft Excel sheet). Enter the values in column I as numbers, and do not enter any formula in this column. The values in column I will be changed to set them to the most optimized values following the process for crashing the project, so our Microsoft Excel sheet looks like this:

	A	B	C	D	E	F	G	H	I	J	K	L	M	N
1	Activity	Description	Duration	Crash Time	Minimum Duration	Maximum Duration	Crash Slope	Predecessor	Crashed Duration	ES	EF	LS	LF	Slack
2	A	Write Instructions	4	1	3	4	$ 400.00		4	1	4	4	7	3
3	B	Select Technique	3	1	2	3	$ 350.00		3	1	3	1	3	0
4	C	Procure Equipment	3	2	1	3	$ 375.00		3	1	3	5	7	4
5	D	Select Operators	4	2	2	4	$ 400.00	B	4	4	7	4	7	0
6	E	Train Operators	2	1	1	2	$ 600.00	D,A	2	8	9	8	9	0
7	F	Install Equipment	2		2	2		C	2	4	5	8	9	4
8	G	Check Procedures	3	1	2	3	$ 200.00	F,E	3	10	12	10	12	0

Figure 5.5: *Crashed Duration initialized to the preset values of Duration for each task*

We know that the project will be scheduled as per the crashed duration, so we will change the formula for calculating **Early Start (ES)**, **Early Finish (EF)**, **Late Start (LS)**, and **Late Finish (LF)** to refer to the **Crashed Duration** values in column I. Enter the formulae in the *table 5.2* in the mentioned cells. Note that the formulae stated in *table 5.2* only apply to this project. For other projects, it must be set as per the discussion in *Chapter 1, Project Scheduling*.

Cell	Formula	Cell	Formula	Cell	Formula	Cell	Formula
J2	1	K2	=J2+I2-1	L2	=M2-I2+1	M2	=L6-1
J3	1	K3	=J3+I3-1	L3	=M3-I3+1	M3	=L5-1
J4	1	K4	=J4+I4-1	L4	=M4-I4+1	M4	=L7-1
J5	=K3+1	K5	=J5+I5-1	L5	=M5-I5+1	M5	=L6-1
J6	=MAX(K2,K5)+1	K6	=J6+I6-1	L6	=M6-I6+1	M6	=L8-1
J7	=K4+1	K7	=J7+I7-1	L7	=M7-I7+1	M7	=L8-1
J8	=MAX(K6,K7)+1	K8	=J8+I8-1	L8	=M8-I8+1	M8	=K8

Table 5.2: *Formulae to calculate Early Start (ES), Early Finish (EF), Late Start (LS), and Late Finish (LF) for the project as stated in figure 5.1*

Tip: The formula for Early Finish (EF) and Last Start (LS) have the same pattern, so they can be entered once and copied to the other rows.

We will add one more column to determine the amount by which the duration of each task has been crashed. We will call this column **Crashed Amount**. Crashed Amount can be calculated by subtracting the **Crashed Duration** (column I) from **Duration** (column C). The updated Microsoft Excel sheet is as shown in *figure 5.6*:

	A	B	C	D	E	F	G	H	I	J	K	L	M	N	O
1	Activity	Description	Duration	Crash Time	Minimum Duration	Maximum Duration	Crash Slope	Predecessor	Crashed Duration	Crash Amount	ES	EF	LS	LF	Slack
2	A	Write Instructions	4	1	3	4	$ 400.00		4	-	1	4	4	7	3
3	B	Select Technique	3	1	2	3	$ 350.00		3	-	1	3	1	3	0
4	C	Procure Equipment	3	2	1	3	$ 375.00		3	-	1	3	5	7	4
5	D	Select Operators	4	2	2	4	$ 400.00	B	4	-	4	7	4	7	0
6	E	Train Operators	2	1	1	2	$ 600.00	D,A	2	-	8	9	8	9	0
7	F	Install Equipment	2		2	2		C	2	-	4	5	8	9	4
8	G	Check Procedures	3	1	2	3	$ 200.00	F,E	3	-	10	12	10	12	0

Figure 5.6: Column to determine the crash amount added

Enter the formulae in *table 5.3* to determine the **Crash Amount**:

Cell	Formula
J2	=C2-I2
J3	=C3-I3
J4	=C4-I4
J5	=C5-I5
J6	=C6-I6
J7	=C7-I7
J8	=C8-I8

Table 5.3: Formulae to calculate the Crash Amount

We will now add one last column to calculate the **Crash Cost**. Crash Cost is the amount of money we would spend to affect the crashing of the tasks. The sum of all the Crash Cost would be the Total Crash Cost for crashing the project. Crash Cost is calculated as the product of the **Crash Amount** and **Crash Slope**. The Microsoft Excel sheet looks like this:

	A	B	C	D	E	F	G	H	I	J	K	L	M	N	O	P
1	Activity	Description	Duration	Crash Time	Minimum Duration	Maximum Duration	Crash Slope	Predecessor	Crashed Duration	Crash Amount	Crash Cost	ES	EF	LS	LF	Slack
2	A	Write Instructions	4	1	3	4	$ 400.00		4	-	$ -	1	4	4	7	3
3	B	Select Technique	3	1	2	3	$ 350.00		3	-	$ -	1	3	1	3	0
4	C	Procure Equipment	3	2	1	3	$ 375.00		3	-	$ -	1	3	5	7	4
5	D	Select Operators	4	2	2	4	$ 400.00	B	4	-	$ -	4	7	4	7	0
6	E	Train Operators	2	1	1	2	$ 600.00	D,A	2	-	$ -	8	9	8	9	0
7	F	Install Equipment	2		2	2		C	2	-	$ -	4	5	8	9	4
8	G	Check Procedures	3	1	2	3	$ 200.00	F,E	3	-	$ -	10	12	10	12	0
9																
10									Total Crash Cost -->	$	-					
11																
12									Project Duration -->		12					

Figure 5.7: Column added to calculate Crash Cost

Enter the formulae in *table 5.4* to calculate the Crash Cost:

Cell	Formula
K2	=J2*K2
K3	=J3*K3
K4	=J4*K4
K5	=J5*K5
K6	=J6*K6
K7	=J7*K7
K8	=J8*K8

Table 5.4: Formula to calculate the Crash Cost

We will calculate the total project crash cost in cell K10. Enter the formula in *table 5.5* to calculate the total project crash cost:

Cell	Formula
K10	=SUM(K2:K8)

Table 5.5: Formula to calculate the Total Project Crash Cost

We will add one last cell to show the total project duration, i.e., cell K12. We know that the total project duration is the day when the last activity in the project network ends, so we can get this value from cell O8. Enter the formula in *table 5.6*:

Cell	Formula
K12	=O8

Table 5.6: Formula to calculate the Total Project Duration

Now, our project is fully set up for crashing. Let's form the linear programming problem for crashing this project.

We need an objective function to set up the linear programming problem. Our objective is to minimize the project duration. We have stored the calculated project duration in cell K12, so we can point to this cell as the objective function. Also, the objective is to minimize.

Next, we need to know which variables we will vary to obtain our solution. We will change the duration of the tasks to minimize the project duration. So, these are available in cells I2 to I8.

Setting these up in Solver will make **Solver Parameters** as shown in *figure 5.8*:

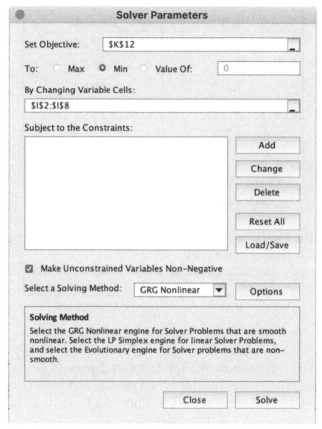

Figure 5.8: *Solver Parameters after setting the objective function and variables to change*

Next, we need to set up the constraints.

The first set of constraints is that the crashed duration should be integers. Set the constraints as shown in *table 5.7*:

Constraints
I2=integer
I3=integer
I4=integer
I5=integer
I6=integer
I7=integer
I8=integer

Table 5.7: *Constraints to set so that the calculated crashed duration are integers*

Solver Parameters will look like this:

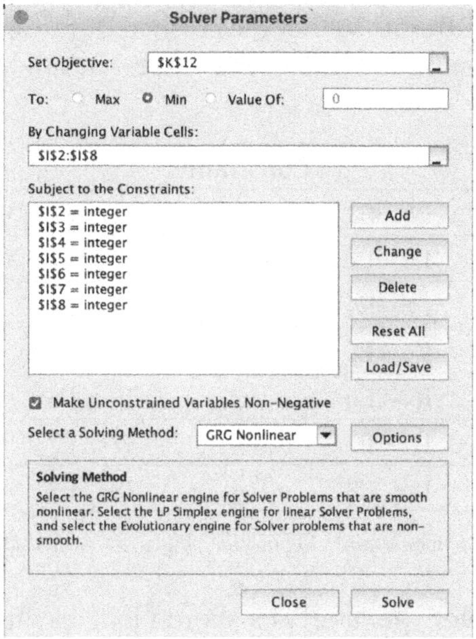

Figure 5.9: *Setting constraints so that the calculated crashed duration is an integer*

We need to do values. Click on the **Options** button on the screen shown in *figure 5.9*. A pop-up will appear, as shown here:

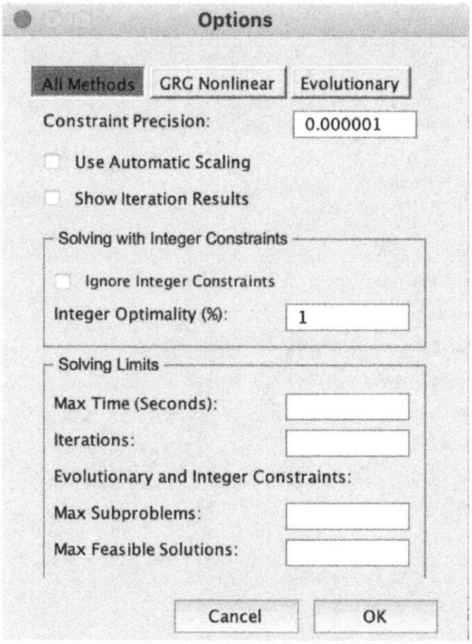

Figure 5.10: *Solver Parameters options pop-up*

Uncheck **Ignore Integer Constraints** and click on **OK** in this pop-up.

Next, we will set the constraints so that the crashed duration is within the minimum allowable values and maximum allowable values. Set the constraints as stated in *table 5.8*:

Constraints	
I2>=E2	I2<=F2
I3>=E3	I3<=F3
I4>=E4	I4<=F4
I5>=E5	I5<=F5
I6>=E6	I6<=F6
I7>=E7	I7<=F7
I8>=E8	I8<=F8

Table 5.8: Constraints to bind the values of Crashed Duration

The complete set of **Solver Parameters** should look as illustrated in *figure 5.11*:

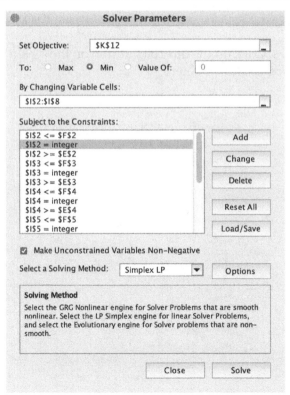

Figure 5.11: Complete Solver Parameter setup for crashing this project

Next, click **Solve** to solve the linear programming problem. The output should look like this:

	A	B	C	D	E	F	G	H	I	J	K	L	M	N	O	P
1	Activity	Description	Duration	Crash Time	Minimum Duration	Maximum Duration	Crash Slope	Predecessor	Crashed Duration	Crash Amount	Crash Cost	ES	EF	LS	LF	Slack
2	A	Write Instructions	4	1	3	4	$ 400.00		3	1	$ 400.00	1	3	2	4	1
3	B	Select Technique	3	1	2	3	$ 350.00		2	1	$ 350.00	1	2	1	2	0
4	C	Procure Equipment	3	2	1	3	$ 375.00		1	2	$ 750.00	1	1	3	3	2
5	D	Select Operators	4	2	2	4	$ 400.00	B	2	2	$ 800.00	3	4	3	4	0
6	E	Train Operators	2	1	1	2	$ 600.00	D,A	1	1	$ 600.00	5	5	5	5	0
7	F	Install Equipment	2		2	2		C	2	-	$ -	2	3	4	5	2
8	G	Check Procedures	3	1	2	3	$ 200.00	F,E	2	1	$ 200.00	6	7	6	7	0
9																
10									Total Crash Cost -->		$ 3,100.00					
11																
12									Project Duration -->		7					

Figure 5.12: Crashed project schedule

Compare the solution in *figure 5.12* with the solution we worked on in the previous chapter. You will see that we could reduce the duration to a minimum of 7 units in the previous chapter, just like *figure 5.12*. We did not proceed with crashing the project when there was no reduction in the duration because of crashing the project. However, in this linear programming problem, we have asked to reduce the duration irrespective of the cost involved, and hence the difference.

Adding constraints for upper limit of crash cost

Let's introduce another constraint to the project, whose solution after crashing is presented in *figure 5.12*. Let the constraint be that the maximum crash amount can be $2,000. To do this, add a constraint in Solver Parameters as shown in *table 5.9*:

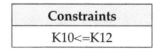

Constraints
K10<=K12

Table 5.9: Constraint to limit the total crash cost

After adding this constraint, solve the linear programming problem. The solution is as shown in *figure 5.13*:

	Activity	Description	Duration	Crash Time	Minimum Duration	Maximum Duration	Crash Slope	Predecessor	Crashed Duration	Crash Amount	Crash Cost	ES	EF	LS	LF	Slack
1																
2	A	Write Instructions	4	1	3	4	$ 400.00		4	-	$ -	1	4	1	4	0
3	B	Select Technique	3	1	2	3	$ 350.00		2	1	$ 350.00	1	2	1	2	0
4	C	Procure Equipment	3	2	1	3	$ 375.00		3	-	$ -	1	3	1	3	0
5	D	Select Operators	4	2	2	4	$ 400.00	B	2	2	$ 800.00	3	4	3	4	0
6	E	Train Operators	2	1	1	2	$ 600.00	D,A	1	1	$ 600.00	5	5	5	5	0
7	F	Install Equipment	2		2	2		C	2	-	$ -	4	5	4	5	0
8	G	Check Procedures	3	1	2	3	$ 200.00	F,E	2	1	$ 200.00	6	7	6	7	0
9																
10									Total Crash Cost -->		$ 1,950.00					
11																
12									Maximum Crash Cost -->		$ 2,000.00					
13																
14									Project Duration -->		7					

Figure 5.13: Crashed project schedule subject to maximum crash cost of $2,000

We will try one more example and consider that the budget for crashing the project is only $1,500, so the maximum crash cost should be less than or equal to $1,500. Enter 1500 in cell K12 in the Microsoft Excel sheet shown in *figure 5.13*. Then, open Solver and solve the linear programming problem. The result is as shown in *figure 5.14*:

	Activity	Description	Duration	Crash Time	Minimum Duration	Maximum Duration	Crash Slope	Predecessor	Crashed Duration	Crash Amount	Crash Cost	ES	EF	LS	LF	Slack
1																
2	A	Write Instructions	4	1	3	4	$ 400.00		4	-	$ -	1	4	1	4	0
3	B	Select Technique	3	1	2	3	$ 350.00		2	1	$ 350.00	1	2	1	2	0
4	C	Procure Equipment	3	2	1	3	$ 375.00		3	-	$ -	1	3	2	4	1
5	D	Select Operators	4	2	2	4	$ 400.00	B	2	2	$ 800.00	3	4	3	4	0
6	E	Train Operators	2	1	1	2	$ 600.00	D,A	2	-	$ -	5	6	5	6	0
7	F	Install Equipment	2		2	2		C	2	-	$ -	4	5	5	6	1
8	G	Check Procedures	3	1	2	3	$ 200.00	F,E	2	1	$ 200.00	7	8	7	8	0
9																
10									Total Crash Cost -->		$ 1,350.00					
11																
12									Maximum Crash Cost -->		$ 1,500.00					
13																
14									Project Duration -->		8					

Figure 5.14: Crashed project schedule subject to maximum crash cost of $1,500

So, we see that subject to a maximum budget of $1,500, we can crash the project so that it can be completed in 8 units of duration.

Crashing the project to a stated duration

Many times, we do not want to crash the project just based on budget. We may have a target that we want to complete the project in a defined duration. For example, let's say we have a target to complete our present project in 10 units (say, 10 weeks).

Project duration is our objective function, so we can set the linear programming problem such that the objective function is set to a defined value. So, in our case, we will state that the objective function should be optimized such that the value of the objective function is 10.

The Solver Parameters is as shown in *figure 5.15* after making this setting:

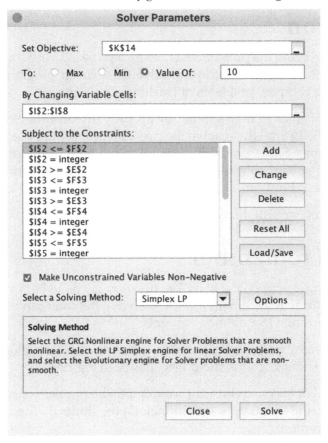

Figure 5.15: *Setting Objective Function to a defined value*

The solution is as shown in *figure 5.16*:

	A	B	C	D	E	F	G	H	I	J	K	L	M	N	O	P
1	Activity	Description	Duration	Crash Time	Minimum Duration	Maximum Duration	Crash Slope	Predecessor	Crashed Duration	Crash Amount	Crash Cost	ES	EF	LS	LF	Slack
2	A	Write Instructions	4	1	3	4	$ 400.00		3	1	$ 400.00	1	3	3	5	2
3	B	Select Technique	3	1	2	3	$ 350.00		2	1	$ 350.00	1	2	1	2	0
4	C	Procure Equipment	3	2	1	3	$ 375.00		3	-	$ -	1	3	3	5	2
5	D	Select Operators	4	2	2	4	$ 400.00	B	3	1	$ 400.00	3	5	3	5	0
6	E	Train Operators	2	1	1	2	$ 600.00	D,A	2	-	$ -	6	7	6	7	0
7	F	Install Equipment	2		2	2		C	2	-	$ -	4	5	6	7	2
8	G	Check Procedures	3	1	2	3	$ 200.00	F,E	3	-	$ -	8	10	8	10	0
9																
10									Total Crash Cost -->		$ 1,150.00					
11																
12									Maximum Crash Cost -->		$ 1,500.00					
13																
14									Project Duration -->		10					

Figure 5.16: *Crashing the project so that the project duration 10 units*

The solution obtained is such that the project duration is 10 units, and the crash cost is less than or equal to $1,500. Remove the constraint on the crash cost and solve the linear programming problem once again. Check whether the solution is different.

Conclusion

Mathematically, solving the problem of crashing a project is very complex. However, using Microsoft Excel's Solver add-in to solve these linear programming problems can make solving complex problems of crashing a project easy.

The Microsoft Excel sheet needs to be set up properly and the Solver Parameters need to be specified correctly to solve the problem of crashing the project. We have seen that we can use Solver to crash a project to the minimum duration, or we can crash the project subject to a maximum crash cost. Alternatively, we can crash a project to a defined duration.

In the next chapter, we will discuss more complex problems of crashing a project.

Points to remember

- In crashing a project, the objective function needs to be set to minimize the project duration. Alternatively, the objective function can be set to crash the project duration to a defined amount.

- In crashing a project, the variable is the crashed duration, i.e., what the duration should be after the project has been crashed.

- Any number of constraints can be added to the problem of crashing a project. However, the constraints should include the limits on the crashed duration at the minimum.

Multiple choice questions

1. **What should be done so that Solver does not bypass the integer constraints?**

    a. The Ignore Integer Constraints checkbox should be checked

    b. The Ignore Integer Constraints checkbox should be unchecked

    c. The Ignore Binary Constraints checkbox should be unchecked

    d. None of these

2. **The number of times Solver should iterate to find a solution can be set in:**

    a. The options pop-up of Solver Parameters

    b. This is not possible to set for Simplex LP method of solving an LPP

    c.   This is only possible to set for Evolutionary method of solving an LPP

    d.   None of these

3.   **What do we need to do to crash a project to a specific duration?**

    a.   Set the Objective Function to minimize

    b.   Set the Objective Function to maximize

    c.   Set the Objective Function to a specific value

    d.   None of these

4.   **What do we need to do to crash a project subject to an upper limit of crash cost?**

    a.   Add a greater than constraint on the calculated crash cost

    b.   Add a lesser than constraint on the calculated crash cost

    c.   Add a lesser than constraint on the calculated project duration

    d.   None of these

5.   **What do we need to do to ensure that the crashed durations are calculated as integers?**

    a.   Round off the crashed durations computed by Solver

    b.   Add constraints so that all the crashed durations are binary

    c.   Add constraints so that all the crashed durations are integers

    d.   None of these

Answers

1. b

2. a

3. c

4. b

5. c

Questions

1. Crash the project stated in figure 5.17 to complete it in the least possible time.

Activity	Duration	Predecessor	Crash Duration	Crash Cost
A	5		2	$ 500.00
B	9	A	3	$ 450.00
C	2	B		
D	3	B	1	$ 600.00
E	17	C,D	5	$ 200.00
F	45	C	10	$ 250.00
H	10	D	2	$ 400.00
J	56	E,R	15	$ 375.00
K	90	F,E	20	$ 350.00
L	32	J,K	4	$ 250.00
R	24	H	6	$ 500.00

Figure 5.17: Project schedule for question 1

2. Crash the project stated in *figure 5.17* such that the total crash cost is less than or equal to $2,000.

3. Crash the project stated in *figure 5.17* such that the total crash cost is less than or equal to $1,000. What changes did make in the Microsoft Excel setup to solve this problem after having solved question 2?

4. Crash the project stated in *figure 5.17* such that the project duration is reduced by 4 units. Is this feasible?

5. Crash the project stated in *figure 5.17* such that the project duration is reduced by at least 10 units and the total crash cost is less than $3,500. Is this feasible?

Key terms

- **LPP**: Linear Programming Problem

CHAPTER 6

More Complex Problems

In the previous chapter, we saw how we can formulate the problem of crashing a project into a linear programming problem and solve it using Microsoft Excel's Solver add-in. Now, we will see more cases of crashing a project subject to different types of constraints.

In the first scenario, we will discuss a project where we need to minimize the company's loss while it is being implemented. We need to find the right point to which the project should be crashed so that the loss is minimal. We will see that always crashing the project to the least possible duration does not provide the best solution.

In the second scenario, we will understand how we can minimize the project cost when there are costs other than the direct cost of conducting the tasks of the project.

The situations discussed in this chapter should be easily relatable from business scenarios. Apart from noticing how the problems are solved, keep an eye on how the Microsoft Excel sheet can be set up so that the problem becomes parameterized and can be used generically by altering values.

Structure

We will discuss the following topics in this chapter:

- **Problem 1:** Minimizing loss during project implementation

- o   Problem definition

- o   Crashing the project to minimum possible duration

- o   Crashing the project such that the net effect is at least 0

- o   Crashing the project such that the net effect is positive

- o   Crashing the project such that the net effect is maximized

- • **Problem 2:** Minimizing the project cost

Objectives

After studying this unit, you should be able to solve various problems around crashing a project. By studying these problems, you should be able to visualize, formulate, and solve other problems related to crashing a project.

Problem 1 – Minimizing loss during project implementation

This first scenario we will consider is from a company facing loss due to non-existence of an essential component. This situation is common in small and large organizations; for example, a bakery may be facing a loss because an essential equipment needs an upgrade. Once the bakery upgrades the equipment, the loss will continue till the project for implementing the new equipment is completed.

Note that most sensible companies undertake projects with an objective in mind. The objective may be to minimize/eradicate loss from current operations, or it can be to enhance the existing capacity. The objective need not always be a tangible outcome, like meeting regulatory requirements. For example, many companies are presently undertaking projects to meet the green initiatives undertaken by the governments. At other times, the objective can be to enhance the company's image or reputation. For example, a company may upgrade its process to meet industry recommended standards.

An essential aspect to note is that no matter what the objective of the company is in undertaking a project, it can be expressed in terms of money. And it is necessary to do so because we must evaluate the success of a project in terms of the throughput it generates. And there is no better measure of throughput than money, as every project involves expenses, which are computed in terms of money.

Problem definition

Now, let's define the problem in terms of numbers. The company in question is facing a loss of $3,500 per week. The loss can be eradicated if it undertakes a project, but the loss will continue till the project is completed.

The initial plan for the project is shown in *figure 6.1*:

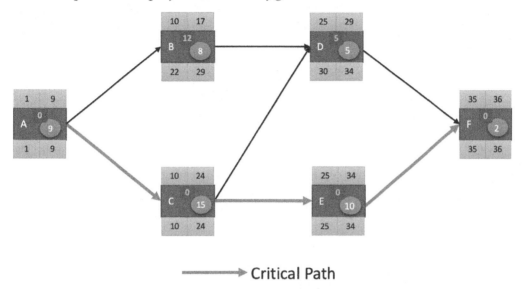

Critical Path

Figure 6.1: Initial project schedule for problem 1

Let's put this plan in a Microsoft Excel sheet and add the necessary information for crashing a project. *Figure 6.2* illustrates this:

	A	B	C	D	E	F	G	H	I	J	K	L	M	N	O
1	Activity	Duration	Crash Time	Minimum Duration	Maximum Duration	Crash Slope	Predecessor	Crashed Duration	Crash Amount	Crash Cost	ES	EF	LS	LF	Slack
2	A	9	6	3	9	$ 3,000.00		9	-	$ -	1	9	1	9	0
3	B	8	5	3	8	$ 3,500.00	A	8	-	$ -	10	17	22	29	12
4	C	15	10	5	15	$ 4,000.00	A	15	-	$ -	10	24	10	24	0
5	D	5	3	2	5	$ 2,000.00	B,C	5	-	$ -	25	29	30	34	5
6	E	10	6	4	10	$ 2,500.00	C	10	-	$ -	25	34	25	34	0
7	F	2	1	1	2	$ 5,000.00	D,E	2	-	$ -	35	36	35	36	0
8															
9								Total Crash Cost -->		$ -					
10															
11								Project Duration -->		36					

Figure 6.2: Project schedule for problem 1 planted on Microsoft Excel

In *figure 6.2*, columns E, I, J, K, L, M, N, and O are computed columns. Let's revisit the formulae required for these computations. Enter the formulae mentioned in *table 6.1* for computing the values in columns E, I, and J:

Cell	Formula	Cell	Formula	Cell	Formula
E2	=B2	I2	=B2-H2	J2	=I2*F2
E3	=B3	I3	=B3-H3	J3	=I3*F3
E4	=B4	I4	=B4-H4	J4	=I4*F4
E5	=B5	I5	=B5-H5	J5	=I5*F5
E6	=B6	I6	=B6-H6	J6	=I6*F6
E7	=B7	I7	=B7-H7	J7	=I7*F7

Table 6.1: Formulae to calculate maximum duration, crash amount, and crash cost

Enter the formulae in *table 6.2* to calculate the **Early Start (ES)** and **Early Finish (EF)** in columns K and L:

Cell	Formula	Cell	Formula
K2	1	L2	=K2+H2-1
K3	=L2+1	L3	=K3+H3-1
K4	=L2+1	L4	=K4+H4-1
K5	=MAX(L3,L4)+1	L5	=K5+H5-1
K6	=L4+1	L6	=K6+H6-1
K7	=MAX(L5,L6)+1	L7	=K7+H7-1

Table 6.2: Formulae to calculate Early Start (ES) and Early Finish (EF)

Enter the formulae stated in *table 6.3* to calculate the **Late Start (LS)** and **Late Finish (LF)** in columns M and N:

Cell	Formula	Cell	Formula
M2	=N2-H2+1	M2	=MIN(M4,M3)-1
M3	=N3-H3+1	M3	=M5-1
M4	=N4-H4+1	M4	=MIN(M6,M5)-1
M5	=N5-H5+1	M5	=M7-1
M6	=N6-H6+1	M6	=M7-1
M7	=N7-H7+1	M7	=L7

Table 6.3: Formulae to calculate Late Start (LS) and Late Finish (LF)

Enter the formulae stated in *table 6.4* to calculate the Slack in column O:

Cell	Formula
O2	=M2-L2
O3	=M3-L3
O4	=M4-L4
O5	=M5-L5
O6	=M6-L6
O7	=M7-L7

Table 6.4: Formulae to calculate Stack

We will calculate the total crash cost in cell J9, so enter the formula mentioned in *table 6.5* in cell J9:

Cell	Formula
J9	=SUM(J2:J7)

Table 6.5: Formula to calculate total crash cost

We will calculate the total project duration in cell J11, so enter the formula stated in *table 6.6* in cell J11:

Cell	Formula
J11	=N7

Table 6.6: Formula to calculate project duration

Now, we will add the remaining parts of our problem to the Microsoft Excel sheet. We can see that the project duration as per the plan is 36 weeks. We will capture this figure in a separate cell (cell J13), as shown in *figure 6.3*. Also, we know that the loss per week is $3,500. We will capture this figure in a separate cell (cell J14), as shown in *figure 6.3*:

	Activity	Duration (weeks)	Crash Time	Minimum Duration	Maximum Duration	Crash Slope	Predecessor	Crashed Duration	Crash Amount	Crash Cost	ES	EF	LS	LF	Slack
2	A	9	6	3	9	$ 3,000.00		9	-	$ -	1	9	1	9	0
3	B	8	5	3	8	$ 3,500.00	A	8	-	$ -	10	17	22	29	12
4	C	15	10	5	15	$ 4,000.00	A	15	-	$ -	10	24	10	24	0
5	D	5	3	2	5	$ 2,000.00	B,C	5	-	$ -	25	29	30	34	5
6	E	10	6	4	10	$ 2,500.00	C	10	-	$ -	25	34	25	34	0
7	F	2	1	1	2	$ 5,000.00	D,E	2	-	$ -	35	36	35	36	0
8															
9							Total Crash Cost -->	$	-						
10															
11							Project Duration -->	36							
12															
13							Normal Project Duration -->	36							
14							Loss per week -->	$ 3,500.00							
15							Number of weeks crashed -->	0							
16							Loss Saved -->	$	-						
17															
18							Net effect of crashing -->	$	-						

Figure 6.3: Rest of the problem planted on the Microsoft Excel sheet

The project duration (captured in the cell J11) should decrease when we crash the project. So, we can get the amount by which the project duration has been reduced by subtracting the crashed project duration from the normal project duration. We will capture this in cell J15. Enter the formula as shown in *table 6.7*:

Cell	Formula
J15	=J13-J11

Table 6.7: Formula to calculate the amount (number of weeks) by which the project has been crashed

When we know the number of weeks that have been reduced from the project duration, we can calculate the amount of loss saved as the product of the loss per week and the number of weeks crashed. We will capture this figure in cell J16; enter the formula as stated in *table 6.8*:

Cell	Formula
J16	=J15*J14

Table 6.8: Formula to calculate the amount saved by crashing the project

Total Crash Cost (cell J9) is the amount of money we spend in crashing the project. Loss Saved (cell J16) is the amount we saved by crashing the project, so we can calculate the net effect of crashing the project by subtracting the Total Crash Cost from the Loss Saved. We will store this in cell J18. Enter the formula as shown in *table 6.9*:

Cell	Formula
J18	=J16-J9

Table 6.9: *Formula to calculate the net effect of crashing the project*

Crashing the project to the minimum possible duration

Now that our problem has been set up, let's crash the project to the minimum possible duration. For this, we must first set up the Solver Parameters to define our linear programming problem.

We want to reduce the project duration to the minimum, so the objective function should be set to minimize the project duration stored in cell J11.

We know that we must vary the variables for the crashed duration or the variables in cells H2, H3, H4, H5, H6, and H7. This can also be written as H2:H7.

Next, we must set up the constraints as stated in *table 6.10*:

Constraints		
$H$2=integer	$H$2<=$E$2	$H$2>=$D$2
$H$3=integer	$H$3<=$E$3	$H$3>=$D$3
$H$4=integer	$H$4<=$E$4	$H$4>=$D$4
$H$5=integer	$H$5<=$E$5	$H$5>=$D$5
$H$6=integer	$H$6<=$E$6	$H$6>=$D$6
$H$7=integer	$H$7<=$E$7	$H$7>=$D$7

Table 6.10: *Constraints for crashing the project to minimize the project duration*

Set the constraint so that the variables are non-negative, and set the option so that the integer constraints are not ignored.

Lastly, set the solving method to Simplex LP and solve the problem.

Note : If setting the solving method to Simplex LP does not produce any result, it is due to the limitations of the machine. In this case, set the solving method to Evolutionary and solve the linear programming problem.

The Solver Parameters should be as depicted in *figure 6.4*:

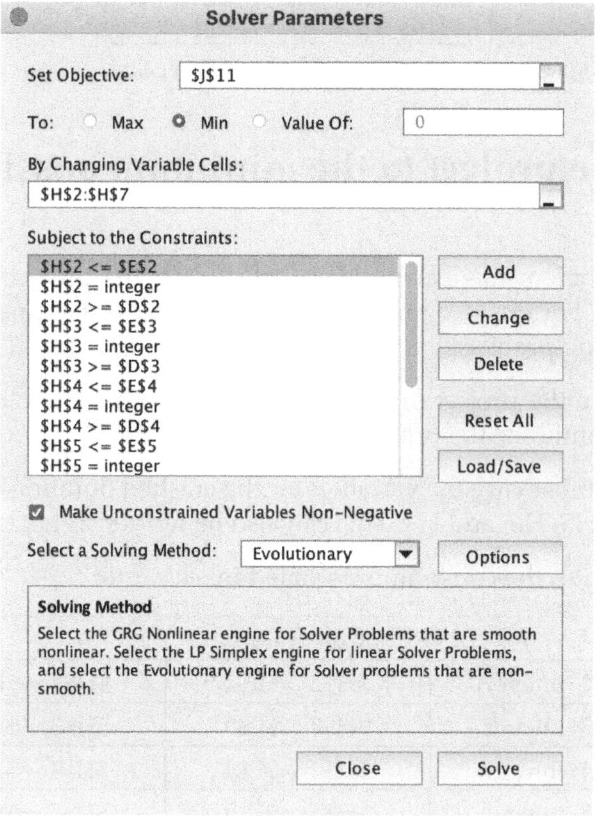

Solver Parameters

Set Objective: $J$11

To: ○ Max   ● Min   ○ Value Of: 0

By Changing Variable Cells:

$H$2:$H$7

Subject to the Constraints:

```
$H$2 <= $E$2
$H$2 = integer
$H$2 >= $D$2
$H$3 <= $E$3
$H$3 = integer
$H$3 >= $D$3
$H$4 <= $E$4
$H$4 = integer
$H$4 >= $D$4
$H$5 <= $E$5
$H$5 = integer
```

Add

Change

Delete

Reset All

Load/Save

☑ Make Unconstrained Variables Non-Negative

Select a Solving Method: Evolutionary ▼   Options

Solving Method

Select the GRG Nonlinear engine for Solver Problems that are smooth nonlinear. Select the LP Simplex engine for linear Solver Problems, and select the Evolutionary engine for Solver problems that are non-smooth.

Close   Solve

Figure 6.4: Solver Parameters

On solving this problem, the result obtained is as shown in *figure 6.5*:

	A	B	C	D	E	F	G	H	I	J	K	L	M	N	O
1	Activity	Duration (weeks)	Crash Time	Minimum Duration	Maximum Duration	Crash Slope	Predecessor	Crashed Duration	Crash Amount	Crash Cost	ES	EF	LS	LF	Slack
2	A	9	6	3	9	$ 3,000.00		3	6	$ 18,000.00	1	3	1	3	0
3	B	8	5	3	8	$ 3,500.00	A	5	3	$ 10,500.00	4	8	6	10	2
4	C	15	10	5	15	$ 4,000.00	A	5	10	$ 40,000.00	4	8	4	8	0
5	D	5	3	2	5	$ 2,000.00	B,C	2	3	$ 6,000.00	9	10	11	12	2
6	E	10	6	4	10	$ 2,500.00	C	4	6	$ 15,000.00	9	12	9	12	0
7	F	2	1	1	2	$ 5,000.00	D,E	1	1	$ 5,000.00	13	13	13	13	0
8															
9								Total Crash Cost -->		$ 94,500.00					
10															
11								Project Duration -->		13					
12															
13								Normal Project Duration -->		36					
14								Loss per week -->		$ 3,500.00					
15								Number of weeks crashed -->		23					
16								Loss Saved -->		$ 80,500.00					
17															
18								Net effect of crashing -->		$ (14,000.00)					

Figure 6.5: Solution when the project in problem 1 is crashed to the minimum duration

We see that the project has crashed to 13 weeks. In other words, the project crashed by 23 weeks. However, we can see that the total crash cost is $94,500 and the net loss saved is $80,500, so the net effect of crashing the project is that we will end up spending $14,000.

Crashing the project so that the net effect is at least 0

The solution in *figure 6.5* results in higher expenses than savings, so it may not be desirable. We must ensure that we do not spend more than what we save because of crashing the project. To achieve this, we will add one more constraint to the Solver Parameters set up to obtain the solution in *figure 6.4*. This is stated in *table 6.11*:

Constraints
J18>= 0

Table 6.11: Additional constraint to ensure that crashing the project does not result in net expense

The **Solver Parameters** will look as illustrated in *figure 6.6*:

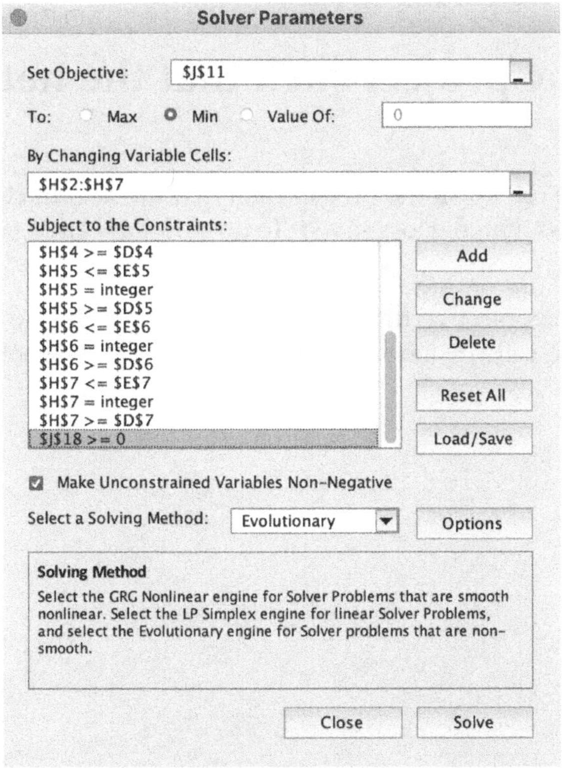

Figure 6.6: Solver Parameters after adding the constraint as stated in table 6.11

Having added the constraint as stated in the *table 6.11* and solved the problem, we get the solution as shown in *figure 6.7*:

	A	B	C	D	E	F	G	H	I	J	K	L	M	N	O
1	Activity	Duration (weeks)	Crash Time	Minimum Duration	Maximum Duration	Crash Slope	Predecessor	Crashed Duration	Crash Amount	Crash Cost	ES	EF	LS	LF	Slack
2	A	9	6	3	9	$ 3,000.00		4	5	$ 15,000.00	1	4	1	4	0
3	B	8	5	3	8	$ 3,500.00	A	7	1	$ 3,500.00	5	11	11	17	6
4	C	15	10	5	15	$ 4,000.00	A	12	3	$ 12,000.00	5	16	5	16	0
5	D	5	3	2	5	$ 2,000.00	B,C	5	-	$ -	17	21	18	22	1
6	E	10	6	4	10	$ 2,500.00	C	6	4	$ 10,000.00	17	22	17	22	0
7	F	2	1	1	2	$ 5,000.00	D,E	1	1	$ 5,000.00	23	23	23	23	0
8															
9								Total Crash Cost -->		$ 45,500.00					
10															
11								Project Duration -->		23					
12															
13								Normal Project Duration -->		36					
14								Loss per week -->		$ 3,500.00					
15								Number of weeks crashed -->		13					
16								Loss Saved -->		$ 45,500.00					
17															
18								Net effect of crashing -->		$ -					

Figure 6.7: *Crashing the project so that the net effect does not result in an expense*

We can see that the net effect of crashing the project is $0 when the project is crashed to 23 weeks, so this is the breakeven point.

Crashing the project such that the net effect is positive

Next, let's see if we can crash the project such that the net effect is positive, i.e., the total crash cost is less than the loss saved. To do so, let's set a $1,000 target for the net effect of crashing.

We must change the objective function to obtain a solution now. We must set the objective function to cell J18 and set it to a value of 1000. The Solver Parameters are shown in *figure 6.8*:

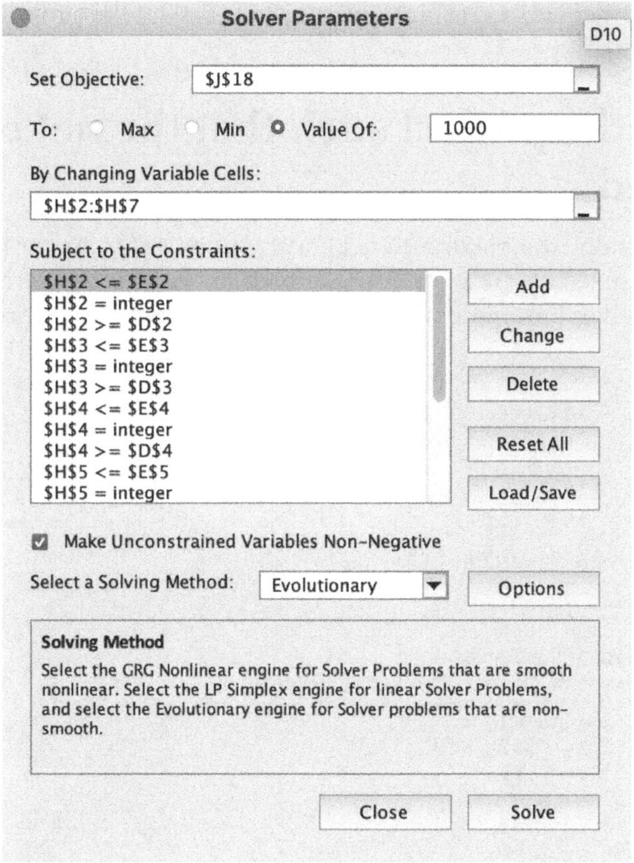

Figure 6.8: *Setting Solver Parameters such that the net effect of crashing the project is $1,000*

On solving the problem now, we get the solution as shown in *figure 6.9*:

	A	B	C	D	E	F	G	H	I	J	K	L	M	N	O
1	Activity	Duration (weeks)	Crash Time	Minimum Duration	Maximum Duration	Crash Slope	Predecessor	Crashed Duration	Crash Amount	Crash Cost	ES	EF	LS	LF	Slack
2	A	9	6	3	9	$ 3,000.00		6	3	$ 9,000.00	1	6	1	6	0
3	B	8	5	3	8	$ 3,500.00	A	8	-	$ -	7	14	10	17	3
4	C	15	10	5	15	$ 4,000.00	A	9	6	$ 24,000.00	7	15	7	15	0
5	D	5	3	2	5	$ 2,000.00	B,C	4	1	$ 2,000.00	16	19	18	21	2
6	E	10	6	4	10	$ 2,500.00	C	6	4	$ 10,000.00	16	21	16	21	0
7	F	2	1	1	2	$ 5,000.00	D,E	2	-	$ -	22	23	22	23	0
8															
9							Total Crash Cost -->			$ 45,000.00					
10															
11							Project Duration -->			23					
12															
13							Normal Project Duration -->			36					
14							Loss per week -->			$ 3,500.00					
15							Number of weeks crashed -->			13					
16							Loss Saved -->			$ 45,500.00					
17															
18							Net effect of crashing -->	$	500.00	= $ 1,000.00					

Figure 6.9: *Solution when we set the objective to obtain a net effect of crashing the project to $1,000*

We see that the net effect of crashing the project is $500 if the project is crashed to 23 weeks.

Crashing the project such that the net effect is maximized

Lastly, let's determine the maximum net effect we can get from crashing this project. We must set the objective function to maximize the net effect of crashing in cell J18 to do this. The Solver Parameters need to be set as shown in *figure 6.10*:

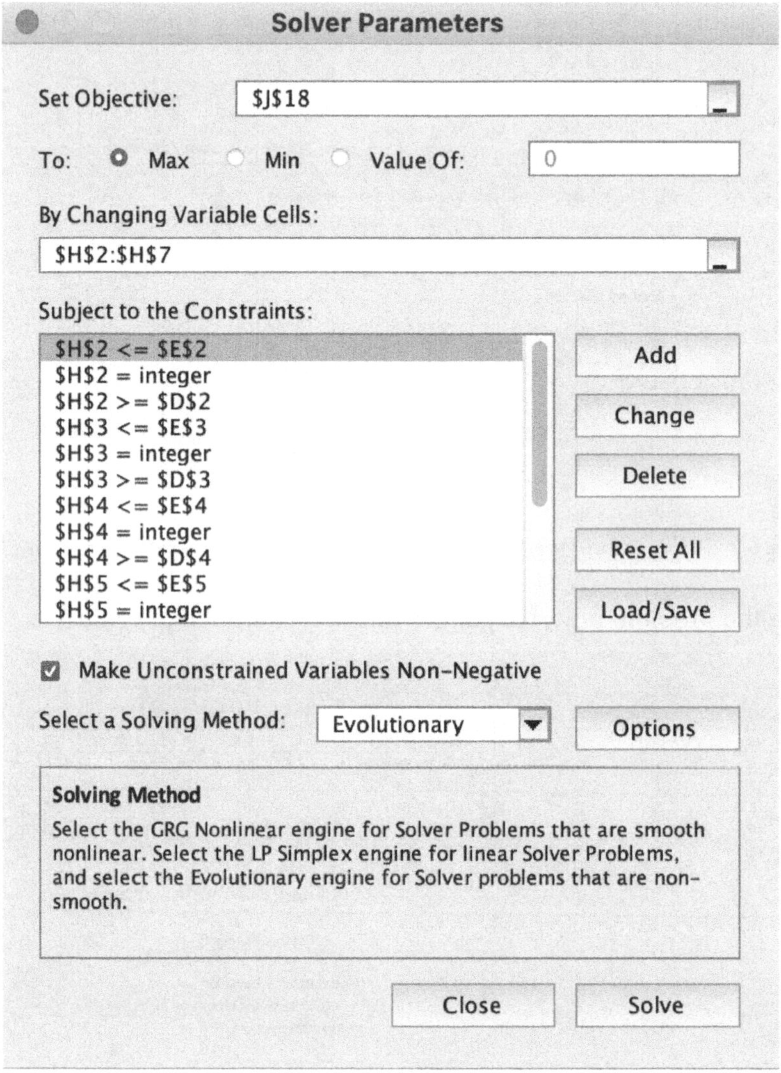

Figure 6.10: *Solver Parameters so that the net effect of crashing the project is maximized*

On solving this problem, we obtain the solution as shown in *figure 6.11*:

	A	B	C	D	E	F	G	H	I	J	K	L	M	N	O
1	Activity	Duration (weeks)	Crash Time	Minimum Duration	Maximum Duration	Crash Slope	Predecessor	Crashed Duration	Crash Amount	Crash Cost	ES	EF	LS	LF	Slack
2	A	9	6	3	9	$ 3,000.00		3	6	$ 18,000.00	1	3	1	3	0
3	B	8	5	3	8	$ 3,500.00	A	8	-	$ -	4	11	7	14	3
4	C	15	10	5	15	$ 4,000.00	A	10	5	$ 20,000.00	4	13	4	13	0
5	D	5	3	2	5	$ 2,000.00	B,C	5	-	$ -	14	18	15	19	1
6	E	10	6	4	10	$ 2,500.00	C	6	4	$ 10,000.00	14	19	14	19	0
7	F	2	1	1	2	$ 5,000.00	D,E	2	-	$ -	20	21	20	21	0
8															
9								Total Crash Cost -->		$ 48,000.00					
10															
11								Project Duration -->		21					
12															
13								Normal Project Duration -->		36					
14								Loss per week -->		$ 3,500.00					
15								Number of weeks crashed -->		15					
16								Loss Saved -->		$ 52,500.00					
17															
18								Net effect of crashing -->		$ 4,500.00					

Figure 6.11: *Crashing the project such that the net effect is maximized*

We can see that the net effect of crashing the project is maximized at $4,500 if this project is crashed to 21 weeks.

The crashed project network is shown in *figure 6.12*:

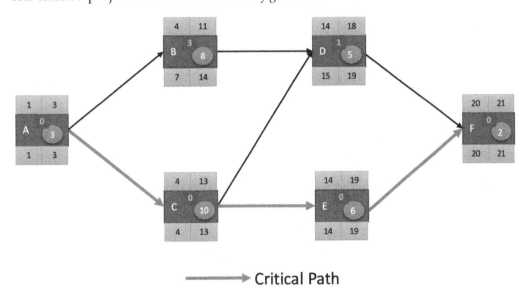

Critical Path

Figure 6.12: *Crashed project network*

Problem 2 – Minimizing the project cost

We consider a situation where the project has direct and indirect costs. We need to minimize the total cost of the project, so we must crash the project to the most optimum point.

Consider that the initial project plan is as shown in *figure 6.13*:

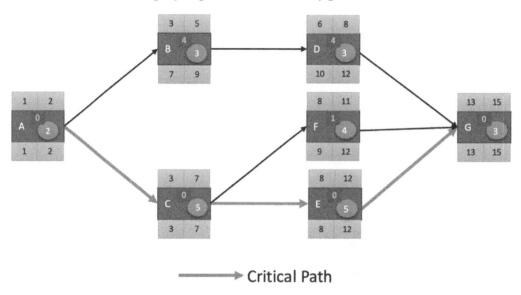

——————➤ Critical Path

Figure 6.13: *Initial project network for problem 2*

The additional information regarding the project is provided in *figure 6.14*:

	A	B	C	D	E	F	G	H	I	J	K	L	M	N	O	P
	Activity	Duration	Cost	Crash Time	Minimum Duration	Maximum Duration	Crash Slope	Predecessor	Crashed Duration	Crash Amount	Crashed Cost	ES	EF	LS	LF	Slack
2	A	2	$ 100.00	0	2	2	$ -		2	-	$ -	1	2	1	2	0
3	B	3	$ 200.00	1	2	3	$ 100.00	A	3	-	$ -	3	5	7	9	4
4	C	5	$ 200.00	1	4	5	$ 40.00	A	5	-	$ -	3	7	3	7	0
5	D	3	$ 200.00	2	1	3	$ 60.00	B	3	-	$ -	6	8	10	12	4
6	E	5	$ 200.00	1	4	5	$ 20.00	C	5	-	$ -	8	12	8	12	0
7	F	4	$ 150.00	1	3	4	$ 40.00	C	4	-	$ -	8	11	9	12	1
8	G	3	$ 150.00	2	1	3	$ -	D,E,F	3	-	$ -	13	15	13	15	0
9	Direct Cost --> $ 1,200.00								Total Crash Cost --> $ -							

	Indirect Cost							Project Duration -->	15	
12	Duration	Amount								
13	11	$ 500.00						Direct Cost	$ 1,200.00	
14	12	$ 550.00						Indirect Cost	$ 700.00	
15	13	$ 600.00						Crash Cost	$ -	
16	14	$ 650.00								
17	15	$ 700.00						Total Cost	$ 1,900.00	

Figure 6.14: *Additional information regarding the project*

Let's go through the components of the information provided.

In column C of *figure 6.14*, we have the cost for every task. So, we can compute the total direct cost of the project by adding the costs of all the tasks. We will calculate the total direct cost in cell C9. Enter the formula in cell C9, as shown in *table 6.12*:

Cell	Formula
C9	=SUM(C2:C8)

Table 6.12: Formula to calculate the total direct cost

For the convenience of performing the remaining calculations, we will copy the value of the total direct cost in cell K13. So, enter the formula as shown in *table 6.13*:

Cell	Formula
K13	=C9

Table 6.13: Copy of the total direct cost

By now, you know how to calculate the values for Minimum Duration, Maximum Duration, Crash Amount, Crash Cost, ES, EF, LS, LF, and Slack. You should also know how to set up cells K9 and K11 to compute the total crash cost and the total project duration, respectively.

So, let's focus on the indirect cost involved in the project. Refer to the table provided in cells B11 to C17 in *figure 6.14*. We see that we have an indirect cost of $500 if the project duration is 11 days. Similarly, we have indirect costs for the project durations of 12, 13, 14, and 15 days.

We will compute the indirect cost for the project in cell K14. The indirect costs are dependent on the total project duration. The total project duration is mentioned in cell K11, so we can look up the value of the total project duration in the table for indirect costs to get the value for the indirect cost. Enter the formula in cell K14 as shown in *table 6.14*:

Cell	Formula
K14	=VLOOKUP($K$11,$B$13:$C$17,2)

Table 6.14: Copy of the total direct cost

The first parameter of the **VLOOKUP()** function is the value to look up. This is the total project duration, and it is available in cell K11.

The second parameter of the **VLOOKUP()** function is the table to look up. This is the table of indirect costs, and it is available in cells B13 to C17. Remember that the first column in **VLOOKUP()** is always searched for the lookup value. So, the lookup value in cell K11 will be searched in cells B13 to B17.

The third parameter of the **VLOOKUP()** function is the column number in the lookup table to pick up the value from. We need the indirect cost, which is stored in the second column of the table (column C). So, we will set the third parameter to 2.

Next, we will make a copy of the total crash cost in cell K15 for our convenience. Enter the formula as shown in *table 6.15*:

Cell	Formula
K15	=K9

Table 6.15: Copy of the total crash cost

Lastly, we will calculate the total project cost in cell K17 by summing up the direct cost, indirect cost, and crash cost. Enter the formula as shown in *table 6.16*:

Cell	Formula
K17	=SUM(K13:K15)

Table 6.16: Formula for the total project cost

Now that our project plan has been set up, let's set up the linear programming problem to obtain the project schedule such that the total project cost is the least.

Our objective is to minimize the total project cost, so the objective function needs to be set to minimize the value in cell K17.

The variables to vary are the crashed duration, which are available in cells I2 to I8.

Lastly, we need to set the constraints as shown in *table 6.17*:

Constraints		
$I$2=integer	$I$2<=$F$2	$I$2>=$E$2
$I$3=integer	$I$3<=$F$3	$I$3>=$E$3
$I$4=integer	$I$4<=$F$4	$I$4>=$E$4
$I$5=integer	$I$5<=$F$5	$I$5>=$E$5
$I$6=integer	$I$6<=$F$6	$I$6>=$E$6
$I$7=integer	$I$7<=$F$7	$I$7>=$E$7
$I$8=integer	$I$8<=$F$7	$I$8>=$E$7

Table 6.17: Constraints for crashing the project to minimize the total project cost

The **Solver Parameters** looks as shown in *figure 6.15*:

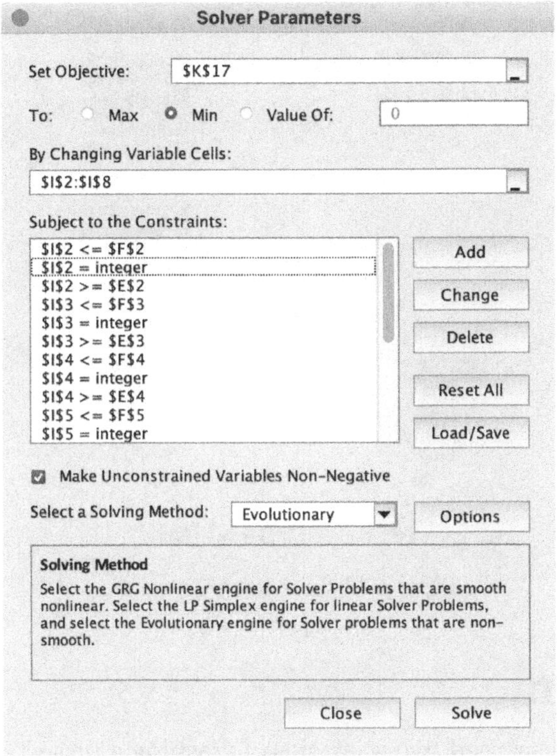

Solver Parameters

Set Objective: $K$17

To: ○ Max   ● Min   ○ Value Of: 0

By Changing Variable Cells:

$I$2:$I$8

Subject to the Constraints:

$I$2 <= $F$2
$I$2 = integer
$I$2 >= $E$2
$I$3 <= $F$3
$I$3 = integer
$I$3 >= $E$3
$I$4 <= $F$4
$I$4 = integer
$I$4 >= $E$4
$I$5 <= $F$5
$I$5 = integer

Add
Change
Delete
Reset All
Load/Save

☑ Make Unconstrained Variables Non-Negative

Select a Solving Method: Evolutionary ▼   Options

Solving Method
Select the GRG Nonlinear engine for Solver Problems that are smooth nonlinear. Select the LP Simplex engine for linear Solver Problems, and select the Evolutionary engine for Solver problems that are non-smooth.

Close   Solve

Figure 6.15: Solver Parameters for problem 2

Remember to set the option to not ignore the integer constraint.

The solution obtained is shown in *figure 6.16*:

	A	B	C	D	E	F	G	H	I	J	K	L	M	N	O	P
1	Activity	Duration	Cost	Crash Time	Minimum Duration	Maximum Duration	Crash Slope	Predecessor	Crashed Duration	Crash Amount	Crashed Cost	ES	EF	LS	LF	Slack
2	A	2	$ 100.00	0	2	2	$ -		2	-	$ -	1	2	1	2	0
3	B	3	$ 200.00	1	2	3	$ 100.00	A	3	-	$ -	3	5	5	7	2
4	C	5	$ 200.00	1	4	5	$ 40.00	A	4	1	$ 40.00	3	6	3	6	0
5	D	3	$ 200.00	2	1	3	$ 60.00	B	3	-	$ -	6	8	8	10	2
6	E	5	$ 200.00	1	4	5	$ 20.00	C	4	1	$ 20.00	7	10	7	10	0
7	F	4	$ 150.00	1	3	4	$ 40.00	C	4	-	$ -	7	10	7	10	0
8	G	3	$ 150.00	2	1	3	$ -	D,E,F	1	2	$ -	11	11	11	11	0
9	Direct Cost -->		$ 1,200.00						Total Crash Cost -->		$ 60.00					
10																
11	**Indirect Cost**								Project Duration -->		11					
12	Duration	Amount														
13	11	$ 500.00							Direct Cost		$ 1,200.00					
14	12	$ 550.00							Indirect Cost		$ 500.00					
15	13	$ 600.00							Crash Cost		$ 60.00					
16	14	$ 650.00														
17	15	$ 700.00							Total Cost		$ 1,760.00					

Figure 6.16: Solution for problem 2

The crashed project network is illustrated in *figure 6.17*:

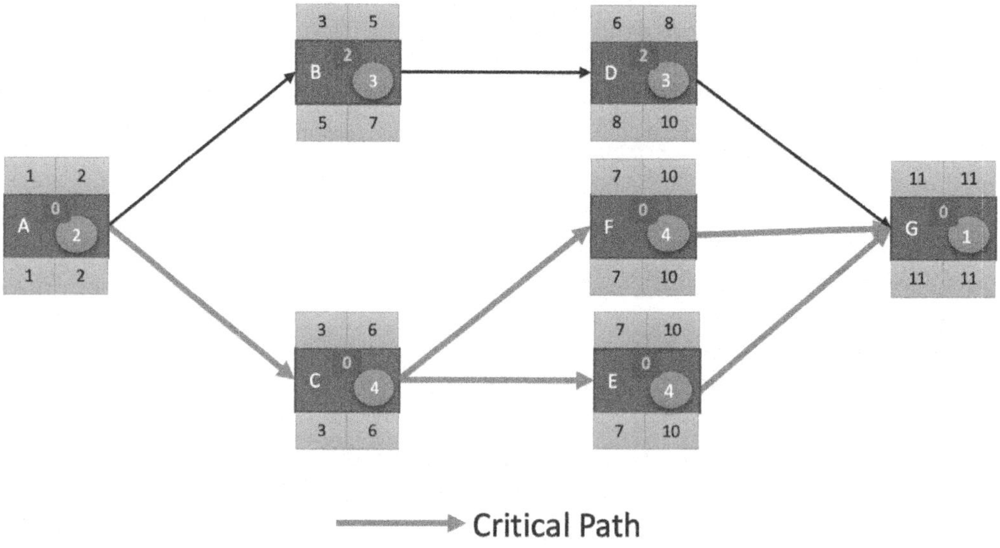

Figure 6.17: Crashed project network

Conclusion

In this chapter we discussed two scenarios of crashing a project. These scenarios are taken from regulation requirements that occur in many organizations. At the very least, the same scenario should be usable by replicating the problem.

However, the bigger picture is that you should be able to formulate linear programming problems for crashing a project for scenarios not covered in this chapter. The process should be mechanical once the concept is clear.

In the next chapter, we will discuss how we can link earned value method with crashing a project. We will then formulate a problem for crashing the project and solve it for the most optimum solution.

Points to remember

- All the problems for crashing a project discussed in this book can be solved using the Simplex method. So, in Microsoft Excel's Solver add-in, if the method for solving is chosen as Simplex LP, a solution should be obtained if there exists a feasible solution. If no solution is obtained by choosing Simplex LP as the method to solve the linear programming problem, it is because of the limitations of the machine. Under this circumstance, try to close all other Microsoft Excel workbooks first and solve the problem. Restart Microsoft

Excel and then try if no solution is produced. If all of this fails, set the method to Evolutionary and solve the problem.

Multiple choice questions

1. **It is always beneficial to crash a project to the maximum extent that the project can be crashed.**

    a. True

    b. False

2. **When we need to get the most beneficial netting value from crashing a project, the optimization operation should be to:**

    a. Maximize

    b. Minimize

    c. Setting to a value

    d. None of these

3. **When we desire the best project cost from crashing a project, the optimization operation should be to:**

    a. Maximize

    b. Minimize

    c. Setting to a value

    d. None of these

Answers

1. b

2. a

3. b

Questions

1. Crash the project in *figure 6.18* such that the net effect of crashing the project is the most beneficial.

	A	B	C	D	E	F
1	Activity	Duration (weeks)	Predecessor	Normal Cost	Crash Time	Crash Slope
2	A	3		$ 10,000.00	3	$ 3,000.00
3	B	7	A	$ 20,000.00	6	$ 4,000.00
4	C	6	A	$ 15,000.00	5	$ 6,000.00
5	D	8	C	$ 45,000.00	6	$ 10,000.00
6	E	9	D	$ 10,000.00	8	$ 2,500.00
7	F	5	B,E	$ 15,000.00	4	$ 4,500.00
8	G	6	D	$ 20,000.00	4	$ 7,500.00
9	H	4	C,E	$ 10,000.00	3	$ 5,000.00
10	I	2	B,E	$ 5,000.00	2	$ 2,500.00
11	J	6	F,G,H,I	$ 40,000.00	5	$ 10,000.00
12	K	3	J	$ 15,000.00	2	$ 12,500.00
13						
14						
15				Loss per week		$ 12,000.00

Figure 6.18: Project plan for question 1

Key terms

*   **Direct cost**: From a project management point of view, any cost essential for the execution of the project is classified as direct cost. Direct costs include the cost of any resources required in the project. For example, in a software development project, the main direct costs would be the cost of manpower for the people working on the project, the cost of the software licenses required for the project, and such. The cost charged by the vendor would be considered as direct cost if the project is partly or fully outsourced. Similarly, in a project to construct a building, the direct costs would include all labor costs, material costs, regulatory expenses, and such.

*   **Indirect cost**: From a project management point of view, any cost that cannot be directly attributed to the project is classified as an indirect cost. Examples of indirect costs include administration costs, security services costs, housekeeping costs, and accounting costs.

CHAPTER 7
Linking
EVM and LPP

So far in the book, we have seen applications of crashing a project as a linear programming problem when we had the initial project schedule for the project. However, we need to crash a project when it is in execution as well. This is because most projects do not go by the plan created for the project, so we may have to plan corrective actions while in execution to put the project back on track.

In *Chapter 2, Earned Value Method*, we discussed how to monitor a project using the **Earned Value Method (EVM)**. We know that EVM gives key indicators in terms of time and cost regarding a project at any particular stage of the project. Using these indicators, we need to decide what corrective measure we need to take.

In this chapter, we will see how to include these indicators from EVM into the project plan and formulate the project schedule into a linear programming problem so that we can optimize the project schedule for time and cost.

To get the maximum value from this chapter, we suggest you to open Microsoft Excel and work along as you read the chapter. Every entry, as required for the calculation, is provided in the text. Once you have gone through the working provided in the chapter, alter some of the figures and check the results; see if we can get a feasible solution in all circumstances.

Structure

We will discuss the following topics in this chapter:

- Setting up the problem
  - Adding components of EVM
  - Calculating EVM indicators
  - Re-estimating the project
- Setting up the LPP to crash the project

Objectives

After studying this unit, you should be able to use Microsoft Excel to formulate a project schedule fit for crashing it as a linear programming problem including considering components of the EVM for project monitoring.

Setting up the problem

Let's start with the project network as shown in *figure 7.1* for our discussions in this chapter:

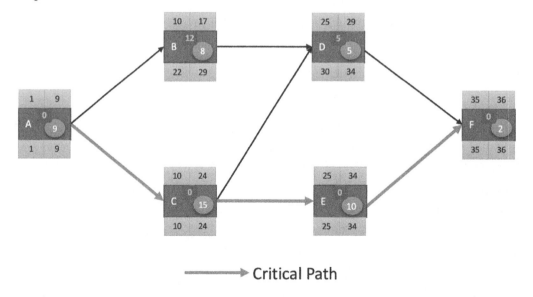

Figure 7.1: Initial project network

We will plant this project network on a Microsoft Excel sheet, as shown in *figure 7.2*:

	A	B	C	D	E	F	G	H	I	J	K	L	M	N	O
1	Activity	Duration	Crash Time	Minimum Duration	Maximum Duration	Crash Slope	Predecessor	Crashed Duration	Crash Amount	Crash Cost	ES	EF	LS	LF	Slack
2	A	9	6	3	9	$ 3,000.00		9	-	$ -	1	9	1	9	0
3	B	8	5	3	8	$ 3,500.00	A	8	-	$ -	10	17	22	29	12
4	C	15	10	5	15	$ 4,000.00	A	15	-	$ -	10	24	10	24	0
5	D	5	3	2	5	$ 2,000.00	B,C	5	-	$ -	25	29	30	34	5
6	E	10	6	4	10	$ 2,500.00	C	10	-	$ -	25	34	25	34	0
7	F	2	1	1	2	$ 5,000.00	D,E	2	-	$ -	35	36	35	36	0
8															
9								Total Crash Cost -->	$	-					
10															
11								Project Duration -->		36					

Figure 7.2: Project network shown in figure 7.1 planted on a Microsoft Excel sheet

The formulae used in creating the Microsoft Excel sheet in *figure 7.2* are repeated here. Make the entries as shown in *table 7.1* to calculate ES and EF:

Cell	Entry	Cell	Entry
K2	1	L2	=K2+H2-1
K3	=L2+1	L3	=K3+H3-1
K4	=L2+1	L4	=K4+H4-1
K5	=MAX(L3,L4)+1	L5	=K5+H5-1
K6	=L4+1	L6	=K6+H6-1
K7	=MAX(L5,L6)+1	L7	=K7+H7-1

Table 7.1: Entries to calculate Early Start (ES) and Early Finish (EF) for the project network shown in Figure 7.1

Make the entries shown in *table 7.2* to calculate **Late Start (LS)** and **Late Finish (LF)**:

Cell	Entry	Cell	Entry
M2	=N2-H2+1	N2	=MIN(M3,M4)-1
M3	=N3-H3+1	N3	=M5-1
M4	=N4-H4+1	N4	=MIN(M5,M6)-1
M5	=N5-H5+1	N5	=M7-1
M6	=N6-H6+1	N6	=M7-1
M7	=N7-H7+1	N7	=L7

Table 7.2: Entries to calculate Late Start (ES) and Late Finish (EF) for the project network shown in figure 7.1

Make the entries as shown in *table 7.3* to calculate Slack:

Cell	Entry
O2	=M2-K2
O3	=M3-K3
O4	=M4-K4
O5	=M5-K5
O6	=M6-K6
O7	=M7-K7

Table 7.3: Entries to calculate Slack for the project network shown in the figure 7.1

We will calculate the Project Duration in cell J11 by making an entry, as shown in *table 7.4*:

Cell	Entry
J11	=N7

Table 7.4: Cell entry to calculate the Project Duration for the project network shown in figure 7.1

Enter the formulae shown in *table 7.5* to calculate the crash amount and the crash cost:

Cell	Entry	Cell	Entry
I2	=B2-H2	J2	=I2*F2
I3	=B3-H3	J3	=I3*F3
I4	=B4-H4	J4	=I4*F4
I5	=B5-H5	J5	=I5*F5
I6	=B6-H6	J6	=I6*F6
I7	=B7-H7	J7	=I7*F7

Table 7.5: Entries to calculate the crash amount and the crash cost

We will calculate the total crash cost in cell J9 by making an entry as shown in *table 7.6*:

Cell	Entry
J9	=SUM(J2:J7)

Table 7.6: Cell entry to calculate the total crash cost

Adding components of EVM

Now, we will add the components of the EVM.

First, let's add the budget for each task and determine the project's **Budget At Completion (BAC)**. Make the entries as shown in *table 7.7*:

Cell	Entry
F2	40000
F3	39000
F4	75000
F5	18000
F6	25000
F7	15000
F9	=SUM(F2:F7)

Table 7.7: Cell entry for Budget At Completion (BAC)

The Microsoft Excel sheet looks as shown in *figure 7.3*:

	A	B	C	D	E	F	G	H	I	J	K	L	M	N	O	P
1	Activity	Duration	Crash Time	Minimum Duration	Maximum Duration	BAC	Crash Slope	Predecessor	Crashed Duration	Crash Amount	Crash Cost	ES	EF	LS	LF	Slack
2	A	9	6	3	9	$ 40,000.00	$ 3,000.00		9	$ -	$ -	1	9	1	9	0
3	B	8	5	3	8	$ 39,000.00	$ 3,500.00	A	8	$ -	$ -	10	17	22	29	12
4	C	15	10	5	15	$ 75,000.00	$ 4,000.00	A	15	$ -	$ -	10	24	10	24	0
5	D	5	3	2	5	$ 18,000.00	$ 2,000.00	B,C	5	$ -	$ -	25	29	30	34	5
6	E	10	6	4	10	$ 25,000.00	$ 2,500.00	C	10	$ -	$ -	25	34	25	34	0
7	F	2	1	1	2	$ 15,000.00	$ 5,000.00	D,E	2	$ -	$ -	35	36	35	36	0
8																
9						BAC $ 2,12,000.00			Total Crash Cost --> $ -							
10																
11									Project Duration -->	36						

Figure 7.3: The Microsoft Excel sheet after adding BAC in column F

We can determine the cost per unit duration of each task once we have the BAC for each task. We will consider that we have consolidated all costs of executing the task in the BAC for each task. Make the entries as shown in *table 7.8*:

Cell	Entry
G2	=F2/B2
G3	=F3/B3
G4	=F4/B4
G5	=F5/B5
G6	=F6/B6
G7	=F7/B7

Table 7.8: Cell entry to calculate the cost per unit duration

The Microsoft Excel sheet will look as shown in *figure 7.4* after adding the column to calculate the cost per unit duration:

	A	B	C	D	E	F	G	H	I	J	K	L	M	N	O	P	Q
1	Activity	Duration	Crash Time	Minimum Duration	Maximum Duration	BAC	Cost per Unit Duration	Crash Slope	Predecessor	Crashed Duration	Crash Amount	Crash Cost	ES	EF	LS	LF	Slack
2	A	9	6	3	9	$ 40,000.00	$ 4,444.44	$ 3,000.00		9	-	$ -	1	9	1	9	0
3	B	8	5	3	8	$ 39,000.00	$ 4,875.00	$ 3,500.00	A	8	-	$ -	10	17	22	29	12
4	C	15	10	5	15	$ 75,000.00	$ 5,000.00	$ 4,000.00	A	15	-	$ -	10	24	10	24	0
5	D	5	3	2	5	$ 18,000.00	$ 3,600.00	$ 2,000.00	B,C	5	-	$ -	25	29	30	34	5
6	E	10	6	4	10	$ 25,000.00	$ 2,500.00	$ 2,500.00	C	10	-	$ -	25	34	25	34	0
7	F	2	1	1	2	$ 15,000.00	$ 7,500.00	$ 5,000.00	D,E	2	-	$ -	35	36	35	36	0
8																	
9						BAC	$ 2,12,000.00			Total Crash Cost --> $ -							
10																	
11										Project Duration -->		36					

Figure 7.4: The Microsoft Excel sheet after adding cost per unit duration in column G

We will consider that the project is in execution, so we will mention the project status at a certain point in time. We will track what was planned for the project at a point of time and the actual status at the same point. So, we will introduce two more columns in the Microsoft Excel sheet: one for capturing the planned completion status and the other for the actual completion status.

Make the entries as shown in *table 7.9*. We will assume that the figures provide the project status. You will have to use information from the project manager and the project team to determine these figures when you are computing status of your project.

Cell	Entry	Cell	Entry
J2	100%	K2	100%
J3	100%	K3	60%
J4	40%	K4	50%
J5	0%	K5	0%
J6	0%	K6	0%
J7	0%	K7	0%

Table 7.9: Cell entry for planned completion and percent completed

The Microsoft Excel sheet will look as illustrated in *figure 7.5*:

	A	B	C	D	E	F	G	H	I	J	K	L	M	N	O	P	Q	R	S
1	Activity	Duration	Crash Time	Minimum Duration	Maximum Duration	BAC	Cost per Unit Duration	Crash Slope	Predecessor	Planned Completion	Percent Completed	Crashed Duration	Crash Amount	Crash Cost	ES	EF	LS	LF	Slack
2	A	9	6	3	9	$ 40,000.00	$ 4,444.44	$ 3,000.00		100%	100%	9	-	$ -	1	9	1	9	0
3	B	8	5	3	8	$ 39,000.00	$ 4,875.00	$ 3,500.00	A	100%	60%	8	-	$ -	10	17	22	29	12
4	C	15	10	5	15	$ 75,000.00	$ 5,000.00	$ 4,000.00	A	40%	50%	15	-	$ -	10	24	10	24	0
5	D	5	3	2	5	$ 18,000.00	$ 3,600.00	$ 2,000.00	B,C	0%	0%	5	-	$ -	25	29	30	34	5
6	E	10	6	4	10	$ 25,000.00	$ 2,500.00	$ 2,500.00	C	0%	0%	10	-	$ -	25	34	25	34	0
7	F	2	1	1	2	$ 15,000.00	$ 7,500.00	$ 5,000.00	D,E	0%	0%	2	-	$ -	35	36	35	36	0
8																			
9						BAC	$ 2,12,000.00					Total Crash Cost --> $ -							
10																			
11												Project Duration -->		36					

Figure 7.5: The Microsoft Excel sheet after adding planned completion in column J and percent completed in column K

Now, we have the necessary information from the project to be able to calculate the **Planned Value (PV)** and **Earned Value (EV)**. So, let's do that in columns L and M. Make the entries as shown in *table 7.10* to calculate the PV in column L and EV in column M:

Cell	Entry	Cell	Entry
L2	=J2*F2	M2	=K2*F2
L3	=J3*F3	M3	=K3*F3
L4	=J4*F4	M4	=K4*F4
L5	=J5*F5	M5	=K5*F5
L6	=J6*F6	M6	=K6*F6
L7	=J7*F7	M7	=K7*F7

Table 7.10: Cell entry to calculate planned value and earned value

We will calculate the PV and EV of the project in cells L9 and M10. Make the entries as shown in *table 7.11*:

Cell	Entry	Cell	Entry
L9	=SUM(L2:L7)	M10	=SUM(M2:M7)

Table 7.11: Cell entry to calculate planned value and earned value for the project

The Microsoft Excel sheet will look as shown in *figure 7.6*:

	A	B	C	D	E	F	G	H	I	J	K	L	M	N	O	P	Q	R	S	T	U
1	Activity	Duration	Crash Time	Minimum Duration	Maximum Duration	BAC	Cost per Unit Duration	Crash Slope	Predecessor	Planned Completion	Percent Completed	Planned Value	Earned Value	Crashed Duration	Crash Amount	Crash Cost	ES	EF	LS	LF	Slack
2	A	9	6	3	9	$ 40,000.00	$ 4,444.44	$3,000.00		100%	100%	$ 40,000.00	$ 40,000.00	9	-	$ -	1	9	1	9	0
3	B	8	5	3	8	$ 39,000.00	$ 4,875.00	$3,500.00	A	100%	60%	$ 39,000.00	$ 23,400.00	8	-	$ -	10	17	22	29	12
4	C	15	10	5	15	$ 75,000.00	$ 5,000.00	$4,000.00	A	40%	50%	$ 30,000.00	$ 37,500.00	15	-	$ -	10	24	10	24	0
5	D	5	3	2	5	$ 18,000.00	$ 3,600.00	$2,000.00	B,C	0%	0%	$ -	$ -	5	-	$ -	25	29	30	34	5
6	E	10	6	4	10	$ 25,000.00	$ 2,500.00	$2,500.00	C	0%	0%	$ -	$ -	10	-	$ -	25	34	25	34	0
7	F	2	1	1	2	$ 15,000.00	$ 7,500.00	$5,000.00	D,E	0%	0%	$ -	$ -	2	-	$ -	35	36	35	36	0
8																					
9					BAC	$ 2,12,000.00				Planned Value (PV)	$ 1,09,000.00			Total Crash Cost -->	$ -						
10										Earned Value (EV)			$ 1,00,900.00								
11														Project Duration -->	36						

Figure 7.6: The Microsoft Excel sheet after adding planned value in column L and earned value in column M

Next, we will calculate the actual cost expended so far in the project. For this, we will add a column to capture the actual duration used to bring the tasks to the current status. Make the entries as shown in *table 7.12*:

Cell	Entry
N2	8
N3	6
N4	12
N5	0
N6	0
N7	0

Table 7.12: Cell entry to capture the actual duration taken by the tasks so far in the project

Once we have the actual durations taken by the tasks, we can compute the **Actual Cost (AC)** expended in the project so far. Make the entries as shown in *table 7.13* to calculate the AC. Actual cost is the product of the actual duration and the cost per unit duration.

Cell	Entry
O2	=N2*G2
O3	=N3*G3
O4	=N4*G4
O5	=N5*G5
O6	=N6*G6
O7	=N7*G7

Table 7.13: Cell entry to calculate the actual cost incurred per task so far in the project

At this stage, we will capture the total actual cost of the project in cell O11. Make the entry as shown in *table 7.14*:

Cell	Entry
O11	=SUM(O2:O7)

Table 7.14: Cell entry to calculate actual cost for the project

The Microsoft Excel sheet looks as follows:

Figure 7.7: *The Microsoft Excel sheet after adding actual duration in column N and actual cost in column O*

Calculating EVM Indicators

We can calculate the indicators from EVM to evaluate our project now that we have the PV, EV, and AC. First, let's calculate **Schedule Variance** (**SV**) and **Cost Variance** (**CV**). This should give an indication of the project in terms of the time and cost.

We know that SV is EV minus PV. We also know that CV is EV minus AC. So, make the entries as shown in *table 7.15* to calculate the SV and CV:

Cell	Entry
L13	=M10-L9
L14	=M10-O11

Table 7.15: *Cell entry to calculate Schedule Variance (SV) and Cost Variance (CV) for the project*

The Microsoft Excel sheet looks as shown in *figure 7.8*:

Figure 7.8: *The Microsoft Excel sheet after calculating the Schedule Variance (SV) and Cost Variance (CV)*

We see that SV and CV are both negative. This indicates that the project is behind schedule and over the budget. We can get an extent of these figures by calculating the **Schedule Performance Index** (**SPI**) and **Cost Performance Index** (**CPI**).

Next, we will calculate SPI and CPI. Make the entries as shown in *table 7.16*:

Cell	Entry
L16	=M10/L9
L17	=M10/O11

Table 7.16: Cell entry to calculate Schedule Performance Index (SPI) and Cost Performance Index (CPI) for the project

The Microsoft Excel sheet looks as follows after making the SPI and CPI calculations:

Figure 7.9: The Microsoft Excel sheet after calculating the Schedule Performance Index (SPI) and Cost Performance Index (CPI)

We can see that this project is behind schedule, but the bigger worry is that the project is heavily over budget at this stage. So, let's see what the **Estimate At Completion (EAC)** is if we assume that the project will progress as per the current levels of performance. We know that EAC is calculated by dividing the BAC by the CPI. Make the entries as shown in *table 7.17* to calculate the EAC:

Cell	Entry
L19	=F9/L17

Table 7.17: Cell entry to calculate Estimate At Completion (EAC) for the project

The Microsoft Excel sheet looks as shown in *figure 7.10*:

Figure 7.10: The Microsoft Excel sheet after calculating the Estimate At Completion (EAC)

In *figure 7.10*, we can see that there will be a cost inflation of more than $50,000 if the project progresses at the current performance levels. So, we need to check if we can take any measures to reduce the cost inflation. From the project scheduling point of view, we can check if we can crash the project to achieve this.

Re-estimating the project

From the current status, the project cannot be completed as per the original schedule of 36 units. Let's re-estimate to see how much time the project will take as per the current situation.

To do this, let's try to establish how much time each of the tasks will take. Now, the tasks that have been completed do not need to be re-estimated. Only the tasks that have not been completed or started have to be estimated. Let's assume that the tasks that have not been started will complete as per the original schedule. There is no reason for us to believe that these tasks will take longer to complete. The only aspect we can be sure about is that the tasks not yet started will start later than the original schedule.

We see that task A has been completed in 8 units as against the planned duration of 9 units, so we need not have to re-estimate this task. However, task B is 60% complete and has consumed 6 units. So, we can re-estimate that task B will take (6/60%*100% =) 10 units to complete. This is against the original plan of completing task B in 8 units.

Enter the formulae as shown in *table 7.18* to calculate the re-estimated duration for each task in column P:

Cell	Entry
P2	=IF(K2>0,ROUND(N2/K2*100%,0),E2)
P3	=IF(K3>0,ROUND(N3/K3*100%,0),E3)
P4	=IF(K4>0,ROUND(N4/K4*100%,0),E4)
P5	=IF(K5>0,ROUND(N5/K5*100%,0),E5)
P6	=IF(K6>0,ROUND(N6/K6*100%,0),E6)
P7	=IF(K7>0,ROUND(N7/K7*100%,0),E7)

Table 7.18: Cell entry to calculate the re-estimated duration for each task

The Microsoft Excel sheet is as shown in *figure 7.11*. A few columns have been hidden in the following Microsoft Excel sheet so that the figures are clearly visible. However, you need not hide any column when working on Microsoft Excel sheets on your computer.

	A	B	C	D	E	F	G	H	I	J	K	L	N	P	Q	R	S	T	U	V	W	X
1	Activity	Duration	Crash Time	Minimum Duration	Maximum Duration	BAC	Cost per Unit Duration	Crash Slope	Predecessor	Planned Completion	Percent Completed	Planned Value	Actual Duration	Forecast Duration	Crashed Duration	Crash Amount	Crash Cost	ES	EF	LS	LF	Slack
2	A	9	6	3	9	$ 40,000.00	$ 4,444.44	$3,000.00		100%	100%	$ 40,000.00	8	8	9	-	$ -	1	9	1	9	0
3	B	8	5	3	8	$ 39,000.00	$ 4,875.00	$3,500.00	A	100%	60%	$ 39,000.00	6	10	8	-	$ -	10	17	22	29	12
4	C	15	10	5	15	$ 75,000.00	$ 5,000.00	$4,000.00	A	40%	50%	$ 30,000.00	12	24	15	-	$ -	10	24	10	24	0
5	D	5	3	2	5	$ 18,000.00	$ 3,600.00	$2,000.00	B,C	0%	0%	$ -	-	5	5	-	$ -	25	29	30	34	5
6	E	10	6	4	10	$ 25,000.00	$ 2,500.00	$2,500.00	C	0%	0%	$ -	-	10	10	-	$ -	25	34	25	34	0
7	F	2	1	1	2	$ 15,000.00	$ 7,500.00	$5,000.00	D,E	0%	0%	$ -	-	2	2	-	$ -	35	36	35	36	0
9					BAC	$ 2,12,000.00				Planned Value (PV)		$ 1,09,000.00			Total Crash Cost -->	$	-					
10										Earned Value (EV)												
11										Actual Cost (AC)					Project Duration -->		36					
13										Schedule Variance (SV=EV-PV)		$ (8,100.00)										
14										Cost Variance (CV=EV-AC)		$ (23,905.56)										
16										Schedule Performance Index (SPI=EV/PV)		0.93										
17										Cost Performance Index (CPI=EV/AC)		0.81										
19										Estimate at Completion (EAC=BAC/CPI)		$ 2,62,227.73										

Figure 7.11: *The Microsoft Excel sheet with the forecast duration calculated in column P*

Next, let's calculate how much each of the tasks can be crashed. This figure will change for the tasks that will take more duration to complete, but it will remain the same for the tasks that have not yet started. Also, this figure is insignificant for the tasks that have already been completed.

We will calculate the new crash duration in column Q. Make the entries as shown in *table 7.19* to calculate the new crash duration:

Cell	Entry
Q2	=ROUND((100%-K2)*C2,0)
Q3	=ROUND((100%-K3)*C3,0)
Q4	=ROUND((100%-K4)*C4,0)
Q5	=ROUND((100%-K5)*C5,0)
Q6	=ROUND((100%-K6)*C6,0)
Q7	=ROUND((100%-K7)*C7,0)

Table 7.19: *Cell entry to calculate the re-estimated duration for each task*

Column K contains the percentage completed for each task, and column C contains the crash time. So, we have proportionately calculated the new crash time as against the original crash time, considering the percentage of the task that has been completed.

The Microsoft Excel sheet looks as shown in *figure 7.12* after calculating the new crash duration:

Activity	Duration	Crash Time	Minimum Duration	Maximum Duration	BAC	Cost per Unit Duration	Crash Slope	Predecessor	Planned Completion	Percent Completed	Planned Value	Actual Duration	Forecast Duration	New Crash Duration	Crashed Duration	Crash Amount	Crash Cost	ES	EF	LS	LF	Slack
A	9	6	3	9	$40,000.00	$4,444.44	$3,000.00		100%	100%	$40,000.00	8	8	-	9	$ -	$ -	1	9	1	9	0
B	8	5	3	8	$39,000.00	$4,875.00	$3,500.00	A	100%	60%	$39,000.00	6	10	2	8	$ -	$ -	10	17	22	29	12
C	15	10	5	15	$75,000.00	$5,000.00	$4,000.00	A	40%	50%	$30,000.00	12	24	5	15	$ -	$ -	10	24	10	24	0
D	5	3	2	5	$18,000.00	$3,600.00	$2,000.00	B,C	0%	0%	$ -	-	5	3	5	$ -	$ -	25	29	30	34	5
E	10	6	4	10	$25,000.00	$2,500.00	$2,500.00	C	0%	0%	$ -	-	10	6	10	$ -	$ -	25	34	25	34	0
F	2	1	1	2	$15,000.00	$7,500.00	$5,000.00	D,E	0%	0%	$ -	-	2	1	2	$ -	$ -	35	36	35	36	0

BAC $2,12,000.00

Planned Value (PV) $1,09,000.00
Earned Value (EV)
Actual Cost (AC)

Total Crash Cost --> $ -
Project Duration --> 36

Schedule Variance (SV=EV-PV) $ (8,100.00)
Cost Variance (CV=EV-AC) $ (23,905.56)

Schedule Performance Index (SPI=EV/PV) 0.93
Cost Performance Index (CPI=EV/AC) 0.81

Estimate at Completion (EAC=BAC/CPI) $2,62,227.73

Figure 7.12: The Microsoft Excel sheet with the new crash duration calculated in column Q

Now that we have established the new duration each task will take and the new crash duration, let's calculate the new minimum duration and the new maximum duration each task will take. The maximum duration is the forecast duration, and the minimum duration is the forecast duration minus the new crash duration. We will calculate these figures in the columns R and S, respectively. Make the entries as shown in *table 7.20* to calculate the new minimum duration and new maximum duration for each task:

Cell	Entry	Cell	Entry
R2	=P2-Q2	S2	=P2
R3	=P3-Q3	S3	=P3
R4	=P4-Q4	S4	=P4
R5	=P5-Q5	S5	=P5
R6	=P6-Q6	S6	=P6
R7	=P7-Q7	S7	=P7

Table 7.20: Cell entry to calculate planned value and earned value

The Microsoft Excel sheet looks as depicted in *figure 7.13*:

Activity	Duration	Minimum Duration	Maximum Duration	BAC	Cost per Unit Duration	Crash Slope	Predecessor	Planned Completion	Percent Completed	Planned Value	Forecast Duration	New Crash Duration	New Min	New Max	Crashed Duration	Crash Amount	Crash Cost	ES	EF	LS	LF	Slack
A	9	3	9	$40,000.00	$4,444.44	$3,000.00		100%	100%	$40,000.00	8	-	8	8	9	$ -	$ -	1	9	1	9	0
B	8	3	8	$39,000.00	$4,875.00	$3,500.00	A	100%	60%	$39,000.00	10	2	8	10	8	$ -	$ -	10	17	22	29	12
C	15	5	15	$75,000.00	$5,000.00	$4,000.00	A	40%	50%	$30,000.00	24	5	19	24	15	$ -	$ -	10	24	10	24	0
D	5	2	5	$18,000.00	$3,600.00	$2,000.00	B,C	0%	0%	$ -	5	3	2	5	5	$ -	$ -	25	29	30	34	5
E	10	4	10	$25,000.00	$2,500.00	$2,500.00	C	0%	0%	$ -	10	6	4	10	10	$ -	$ -	25	34	25	34	0
F	2	1	2	$15,000.00	$7,500.00	$5,000.00	D,E	0%	0%	$ -	2	1	1	2	2	$ -	$ -	35	36	35	36	0

BAC $2,12,000.00

Planned Value (PV) $1,09,000.00
Earned Value (EV)
Actual Cost (AC)

Total Crash Cost --> $ -
Project Duration --> 36

Schedule Variance (SV=EV-PV) $ (8,100.00)
Cost Variance (CV=EV-AC) $ (23,905.56)

Schedule Performance Index (SPI=EV/PV) 0.93
Cost Performance Index (CPI=EV/AC) 0.81

Estimate at Completion (EAC=BAC/CPI) $2,62,227.73

Figure 7.13: The Microsoft Excel sheet with the new minimum duration and new maximum duration for each task calculated in the columns R and S, respectively

Let's store the original project duration in a separate cell. We will need this figure to see the impact of crashing a project. We can then determine whether crashing the project is actually useful. We will record the original project duration in cell V13. Make the entry as shown in *table 7.21* to store the original project duration:

Cell	Entry
V13	36

Table 7.21: Cell entry to store the original project duration

The Microsoft Excel sheet looks as shown in *figure 7.14*:

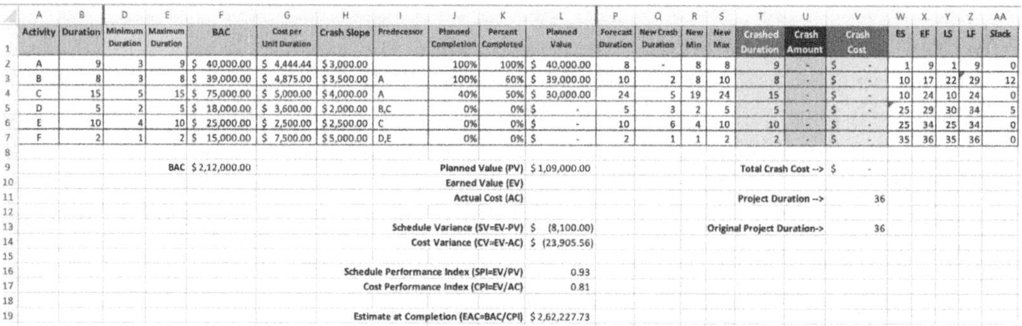

Figure 7.14: The Microsoft Excel sheet with the original project duration stored in cell V13

Next, we will assume that the project will proceed as per the forecasted duration. So, we will update the column containing the crashed duration with the values in the forecasted duration. The crash amount needs to be recalculated with respect to the forecast duration. Make the entries as shown in *table 7.22*:

Cell	Entry	Cell	Entry
T2	8	U2	=P2-T2
T3	10	U3	=P3-T3
T4	24	U4	=P4-T4
T5	5	U5	=P5-T5
T6	10	U6	=P6-T6
T7	2	U7	=P7-T7

Table 7.22: Cell entry to set the crashed duration as the figures calculated for forecasted duration

The Microsoft Excel sheet looks as shown in *figure 7.15*:

Activity	Duration	Minimum Duration	Maximum Duration	BAC	Cost per Unit Duration	Crash Slope	Predecessor	Planned Completion	Percent Completed	Planned Value	Forecast Duration	New Crash Duration	New Min	New Max	Crashed Duration	Crash Amount	Crash Cost	ES	EF	LS	LF	Slack
A	9	3	9	$ 40,000.00	$ 4,444.44	$3,000.00		100%	100%	$ 40,000.00	8	-	8	8	8	•	$ -	1	8	1	8	0
B	8	3	8	$ 39,000.00	$ 4,875.00	$3,500.00	A	100%	60%	$ 39,000.00	10	2	8	10	10	•	$ -	9	18	28	37	19
C	15	5	15	$ 75,000.00	$ 5,000.00	$4,000.00	A	40%	50%	$ 30,000.00	24	5	19	24	24	-	$ -	9	32	9	32	0
D	5	2	5	$ 18,000.00	$ 3,600.00	$2,000.00	B,C	0%	0%	$ -	5	3	2	5	5	•	$ -	33	37	38	42	5
E	10	4	10	$ 25,000.00	$ 2,500.00	$2,500.00	C	0%	0%	$ -	10	6	4	10	10	•	$ -	33	42	33	42	0
F	2	1	2	$ 15,000.00	$ 7,500.00	$5,000.00	D,E	0%	0%	$ -	2	1	1	2	2	-	$ -	43	44	43	44	0

BAC $2,12,000.00

Planned Value (PV) $1,09,000.00
Earned Value (EV)
Actual Cost (AC)

Schedule Variance (SV=EV-PV) $ (8,100.00)
Cost Variance (CV=EV-AC) $ (23,905.56)

Schedule Performance Index (SPI=EV/PV) 0.93
Cost Performance Index (CPI=EV/AC) 0.81

Estimate at Completion (EAC=BAC/CPI) $2,62,227.73

Total Crash Cost --> $ -
Project Duration --> 44
Original Project Duration-> 36

Figure 7.15: *The Microsoft Excel sheet after resetting the crash duration and recalculating the crash amount with respect to the forecasted duration*

We know that when we use Solver, we can set the option so that Solver does not violate the integer restriction. While Solver tries to adhere to the constraints, there are times when it fails to meet all of them. So, we will take a precautionary step by introducing a new column to store the rounded figure of the crashed duration. Make the entries as shown in *table 7.23* to store the rounded value of the crashed duration:

Cell	Entry
U2	=ROUND(T2,0)
U3	=ROUND(T3,0)
U4	=ROUND(T4,0)
U5	=ROUND(T5,0)
U6	=ROUND(T6,0)
U7	=ROUND(T7,0)

Table 7.23: *Cell entry to store the rounded figures for the crashed duration in column U*

The Microsoft Excel sheet looks as illustrated in *figure 7.16*:

Activity	Duration	Minimum Duration	Maximum Duration	BAC	Cost per Unit Duration	Crash Slope	Predecessor	Planned Value	Forecast Duration	New Crash Duration	New Min	New Max	Crashed Duration	Round	Crash Amount	Crash Cost	ES	EF	LS	LF	Slack
A	9	3	9	$ 40,000.00	$ 4,444.44	$3,000.00		$ 40,000.00	8	-	8	8	8	8	-	$ -	1	8	1	8	0
B	8	3	8	$ 39,000.00	$ 4,875.00	$3,500.00	A	$ 39,000.00	10	2	8	10	10	10	-	$ -	9	18	28	37	19
C	15	5	15	$ 75,000.00	$ 5,000.00	$4,000.00	A	$ 30,000.00	24	5	19	24	24	24	-	$ -	9	32	9	32	0
D	5	2	5	$ 18,000.00	$ 3,600.00	$2,000.00	B,C	$ -	5	3	2	5	5	5	-	$ -	33	37	38	42	5
E	10	4	10	$ 25,000.00	$ 2,500.00	$2,500.00	C	$ -	10	6	4	10	10	10	-	$ -	33	42	33	42	0
F	2	1	2	$ 15,000.00	$ 7,500.00	$5,000.00	D,E	$ -	2	1	1	2	2	2	-	$ -	43	44	43	44	0

BAC $2,12,000.00

d Value (PV) $1,09,000.00
d Value (EV)
ual Cost (AC)

(SV=EV-PV) $ (8,100.00)
(CV=EV-AC) $ (23,905.56)

mance Index (SPI=EV/PV) 0.93
mance Index (CPI=EV/AC) 0.81

ompletion (EAC=BAC/CPI) $2,62,227.73

Total Crash Cost --> $ -
Project Duration --> 44
Original Project Duration-> 36

Figure 7.16: *The Microsoft Excel sheet after storing the rounded value of the crash duration*

Now that we have all the essentials, let's calculate the forecasted cost of the project under the forecasted duration. Forecasted cost is the forecasted duration multiplied by the cost per unit duration. We are going to vary the crashed duration, so we will use these values as the forecasted duration. Further, we have stored the integer value of the forecasted duration (rounded value of crashed duration) in column U. So, we will use these values to calculate the forecasted cost. Make the entries as shown in *table 7.24* to calculate the forecasted cost:

Cell	Entry
T2	=V2*G2
T3	=V3*G3
T4	=V4*G4
T5	=V5*G5
T6	=V6*G6
T7	=V7*G7

Table 7.24: Cell entry to calculate the forecasted cost in column T

We can now calculate the new forecasted project cost as the sum of the forecasted cost of all the tasks. We can also calculate the total project cost, which is the sum of the forecasted project cost and the crash cost. Lastly, we can calculate the cost inflation as the difference between the total project cost and the budget at completion. Make the entries as shown in *table 7.25*:

Cell	Entry
T2	=SUM(T2:T7)
T3	=T9+X9
T4	=T11-F9

Table 7.25: Cell entry to store the forecasted project cost, total project cost, and cost inflation

The Microsoft Excel sheet will look as shown in *figure 7.17*:

	A	B	D	E	F	G	H	I	L	P	Q	R	S	T	U	V	W	X	Y	Z	AA	AB	AC
1	Activity	Duration	Minimum Duration	Maximum Duration	BAC	Cost per Unit Duration	Crash Slope	Predecessor	Planned Value	Forecast Duration	New Crash Duration	New Min	New Max	Forecast Cost	Crashed Duration	Round	Crash Amount	Crash Cost	ES	EF	LS	LF	Slack
2	A	9	3	9	$ 40,000.00	$ 4,444.44	$3,000.00		$ 40,000.00	8	-	8	8	$ 35,555.56	8	8	-	$ -	1	8	1	8	0
3	B	8	3	8	$ 39,000.00	$ 4,875.00	$3,500.00	A	$ 39,000.00	10	2	8	10	$ 48,750.00	10	10	-	$ -	9	18	28	37	19
4	C	15	5	15	$ 75,000.00	$ 5,000.00	$4,000.00	A	$ 30,000.00	24	5	19	24	$1,20,000.00	24	24	-	$ -	9	32	9	32	0
5	D	5	2	5	$ 18,000.00	$ 3,600.00	$2,000.00	B,C	$ -	5	3	2	5	$ 18,000.00	5	5	-	$ -	33	37	38	42	5
6	E	10	4	10	$ 25,000.00	$ 2,500.00	$2,500.00	C	$ -	10	6	4	10	$ 25,000.00	10	10	-	$ -	33	42	33	42	0
7	F	2	1	2	$ 15,000.00	$ 7,500.00	$5,000.00	D,E	$ -	2	1	1	2	$ 15,000.00	2	2	-	$ -	43	44	43	44	0
8																							
9					BAC $ 2,12,000.00		d Value (PV)	$ 1,09,000.00			Forecast Cost -->	$ 2,62,305.56			Total Crash Cost --> $ -								
10							d Value (EV)																
11							ual Cost (AC)				Total Cost -->	$ 2,62,305.56			Project Duration -->	44							
12																							
13							(SV=EV-PV)	$ (8,100.00)			Cost Inflation -->	$ 50,305.56			Original Project Duration->	36							
14							(CV=EV-AC)	$ (23,905.56)															
15																							
16							mance Index (SPI=EV/PV)	0.93															
17							mance Index (CPI=EV/AC)	0.81															
18																							
19							ompletion (EAC=BAC/CPI)	$ 2,62,227.73															

Figure 7.17: The Microsoft Excel sheet after the calculations for forecasted project cost, total project cost, and cost inflation

Setting up the LPP to crash the project

We can see that the **Total Cost** as shown in *figure 7.17* is nearly the same as the **Estimate at Completion (EAC)**. There is a cost inflation of over $50,000, so we need to determine if we can reduce the cost of the project by trying to crash it.

Let's set up the LPP for crashing the project.

We have to minimize the total project cost, so the objective function needs to be set at cell T11.

The variables to change are the Crashed Duration, which are available in cells U2 through U7.

Set the constraints as shown in *table 7.26* to ensure that the calculated Crashed Duration are integers:

Constraint
U2 = Integer
U3 = Integer
U4 = Integer
U5 = Integer
U6 = Integer
U7 = Integer

Table 7.26: Constraints for Solver to ensure that the calculated Crashed Duration are integers

Set the constraints as shown in *table 7.27* to ensure that the calculated Crashed Duration is greater than or equal to the new minimum duration and less than or equal to the new maximum duration.

Constraint	
U2 >= R2	U2 <= S2
U3 >= R3	U3 <= S3
U4 >= R4	U4 <= S4
U5 >= R5	U5 <= S5
U6 >= R6	U6 <= S6
U7 >= R7	U7 <= S7

Table 7.27: Constraints for Solver to ensure that the calculated Crashed Duration are within bounds

The **Solver Parameters** will look as shown in *figure 7.18*:

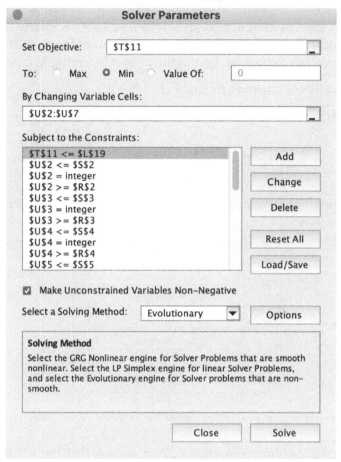

Figure 7.18: Solver Parameters

We get the following result on solving this linear programming problem:

	A	B	F	G	H	I	L	P	Q	R	S	T	U	V	W	X	Y	Z	AA	AB	AC
1	Activity	Duration	BAC	Cost per Unit Duration	Crash Slope	Predecessor	Planned Value	Forecast Duration	New Crash Duration	New Min	New Max	Forecast Cost	Crashed Duration	Round	Crash Amount	Crash Cost	ES	EF	LS	LF	Slack
2	A	9	$ 40,000.00	$ 4,444.44	$3,000.00		$ 40,000.00	8	-	8	8	$ 35,555.56	8	8	$ -	$ -	1	8	1	8	0
3	B	8	$ 39,000.00	$ 4,875.00	$3,500.00	A	$ 39,000.00	10	2	8	10	$ 39,000.00	8	8	2	$ 7,000.00	9	16	27	34	18
4	C	15	$ 75,000.00	$ 5,000.00	$4,000.00	A	$ 30,000.00	24	5	19	24	$ 95,000.00	19	19	5	$ 20,000.00	9	27	9	27	0
5	D	5	$ 18,000.00	$ 3,600.00	$2,000.00	B,C	$ -	5	3	2	5	$ 7,200.00	2	2	3	$ 6,000.00	28	29	35	36	7
6	E	10	$ 25,000.00	$ 2,500.00	$2,500.00	C	$ -	10	6	4	10	$ 22,500.00	9	9	1	$ 2,500.00	28	36	28	36	0
7	F	2	$ 15,000.00	$ 7,500.00	$5,000.00	D,E	$ -	2	1	1	2	$ 7,500.00	1	1	1	$ 5,000.00	37	37	37	37	0
8																					
9			$ 2,12,000.00			d Value (PV)	$1,09,000.00		Forecast Cost -->		$ 2,06,755.56		Total Crash Cost -->	$ 40,500.00							
10						d Value (EV)															
11						ual Cost (AC)			Total Cost -->		$ 2,47,255.56		Project Duration -->	37							
12																					
13						(SV=EV-PV)	$ (8,100.00)		Cost Inflation -->		$ 35,255.56	Original Project Duration->	36								
14						(CV=EV-AC)	$ (23,905.56)														
15													Project Delay -->	1							
16						mance Index (SPI=EV/PV)	0.93														
17						mance Index (CPI=EV/AC)	0.81														
18																					
19						ompletion (EAC=BAC/CPI)	$ 2,62,227.73														

Figure 7.19: Crashed project schedule

We can see that the project will take 37 units instead of 44 units on crashing it. Also, we can see that the cost inflation is about $ 35,000 instead of about $ 50,000, so it makes sense to crash the project in this case.

It needs noting that we may not obtain a feasible solution in all such circumstances. In those circumstances, we cannot crash the project.

Conclusion

In this chapter, we discussed two significant aspects. The first aspect we discussed is that we may have to replan the project during its execution to put it back on track. This is a common requirement in almost all projects, and the projects that execute exactly as per the plan are outliers.

The second aspect we discussed is how to crash a project that is in execution. We saw that the project we discussed had some parts of activities either fully or partially completed. Under these circumstances, we need many other considerations to set up a project for crashing.

From these two aspects, you would have realized that the mathematical form of the linear programming problem is extremely complex and difficult to solve using paper and pencil. So, we need tools like Microsoft Excel's Solver to solve such linear programming problems.

With this chapter, we conclude this book on crashing a project.

Points to remember

- We need to use the EVM to establish the current status of a project. EVM is a very good tool for project monitoring as it totally depends on data. This means subjectivity in evaluating a project is taken away.

- We discussed one method of formulating the linear programming problem for crashing the project linking earned value method in this chapter. The steps need careful examination. The main reason for studying this is to understand how to connect the various aspects of EVM to the objective function.

Multiple choice questions

1. Suppose the original duration of a task is 10 weeks, the task is 60% complete, and the actual duration consumed is 12 weeks. What is the forecasted duration for the task?

    a. 10 weeks

    b. 12 weeks

   c.   14 weeks

   d.   None of these

2.   **Suppose PV = $50,000, EV = $60,000, AC = 45,000, then:**

   a.   SV = $ 15,000

   b.   CV = $ 15,000

   c.   CV = $ 10,000

   d.   None of these

3.   **Suppose PV = $50,000, EV = $60,000, AC = 45,000, then:**

   a.   SPI = 1.2

   b.   CPI = 1.2

   c.   SPI = 0.833

   d.   None of these

4.   **Suppose PV = $50,000, EV = $60,000, AC = 45,000, BAC = $1,00,000, then:**

   a.   EAC = $ 83,333.33

   b.   EAC = $ 60,000

   c.   EAC = $ 75,000

   d.   None of these

5.   **Suppose PV = $50,000, EV = $60,000, AC = 45,000, BAC = $1,00,000, then:**

   a.   The project is over budget

   b.   The project is ahead of schedule

   c.   The project is behind schedule

Answers

1.   b

2.   b

3.   a

4.   c

5.   b

Questions

1. Determine the current status of the project provided in *figure 7.20*. Does this project need to be crashed? Crash the project to the maximum profitability. Can we get a feasible solution on crashing the project?

	A	B	C	D	E	F	G	H
1	Activity	Duration	Crash Time	BAC	Crash Slope	Predecessor	Planned Completion	Percent Completed
2	A	9	6	$ 40,000.00	$ 3,000.00		100%	100%
3	B	8	5	$ 45,000.00	$ 3,500.00	A	100%	90%
4	C	15	10	$ 95,000.00	$ 4,000.00	A	40%	50%
5	D	5	3	$ 15,000.00	$ 2,000.00	B,C	20%	10%
6	E	10	6	$ 25,000.00	$ 2,500.00	C	0%	0%
7	F	2	1	$ 15,000.00	$ 5,000.00	D,E	0%	0%

Figure 7.20: Project schedule for question 1

2. Determine the current status of the project provided in *figure 7.21*. Does this project need to be crashed? Crash the project to the maximum profitability. Can we get a feasible solution on crashing the project?

	A	B	C	D	E	F	G	H
1	Activity	Duration	Crash Time	BAC	Crash Slope	Predecessor	Planned Completion	Percent Completed
2	A	9	6	$ 25,000.00	$ 3,000.00		100%	100%
3	B	8	5	$ 30,000.00	$ 3,500.00	A	100%	80%
4	C	15	10	$ 50,000.00	$ 4,000.00	A	40%	50%
5	D	5	3	$ 10,000.00	$ 2,000.00	B,C	20%	15%
6	E	10	6	$ 20,000.00	$ 2,500.00	C	0%	0%
7	F	2	1	$ 8,000.00	$ 5,000.00	D,E	0%	0%

Figure 7.21: Project schedule for question 2

Key terms

- **LPP**: Linear Programming Problem
- **EVM**: Earned Value Method
- **PV**: Planned Value
- **EV**: Earned Value
- **AC**: Actual Cost

- **SV**: Schedule Variance
- **CV**: Cost Variance
- **SPI**: Schedule Performance Index
- **CPI**: Cost Performance Index
- **BAC**: Budget At Completion
- **EAC**: Estimate At Completion

Annexure 1

We have used Microsoft Excel as the spreadsheet program for solving program scheduling problems. Microsoft Excel is a very popular tool, and everyone is expected to be familiar with it. However, if some readers have never used a spreadsheet or Microsoft Excel before reading this book, this annexure provides the essential knowledge to be able to use Microsoft Excel. It is a vast software with many features. This annexure will cover the features of Microsoft Excel required to be able to understand the concepts discussed in this book.

This annexure should provide a smooth transition to Microsoft Excel for readers who have never used Microsoft Excel but have used other spreadsheet programs like Numbers on Apple Mac. The concepts of spreadsheets across all such tools remains the same, but the implementation will differ.

Structure

We will discuss the following topics in this chapter:

- Spreadsheet basics
  - Filling values in cells
  - Using formula
  - Using Microsoft Excel built-in functions

  o Relative addressing

  o Absolute addressing

Objectives

After studying this unit, you should be able to use Microsoft Excel for performing basic spreadsheet activities.

Spreadsheet basics

Spreadsheets were invented by *Dan Bricklin* in 1979. Over the years, spreadsheets have become one of the fundamental software used by computer users. Spreadsheets have evolved over the years, but the fundamental idea remains the same. They are used by school students as well as fortune 500 companies.

A spreadsheet is an array of cells on a two-dimension space. The cells are identified by two identifiers, called the **row** and **column**. So, a spreadsheet has rows and columns. A row intersects a column at every point, and this point is called a cell. Specifically, in Microsoft Excel, the columns are numbered using alphabets like A, B, C, and so on, and the rows are numbered using digits like 1, 2, 3, and so on. So, the point where column A intersects row 3 is called cell A3. An empty sheet from Microsoft Excel is displayed in *figure A1.1*, and the cursor is placed on cell A3:

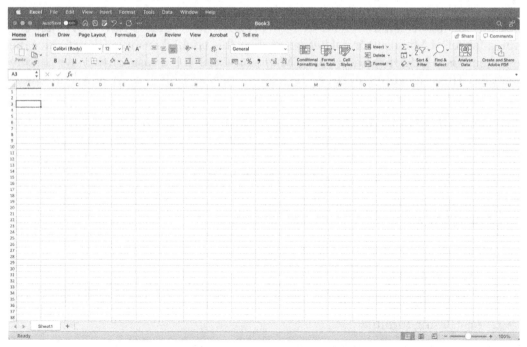

***Figure A1.1**: Microsoft Excel sheet with cursor on cell A3*

In *figure A1.1*, you can see that column name A and row name 3 are in green, while the rest of the column and row names are in black. You will see a green rectangle around cell A3 when you use Microsoft Excel and click on cell A3. Note that A3 is displayed in the top left corner under the menu. This states that A3 is the currently selected cell.

You can use the arrow keys on the keyboard to move between the cells. As you move between the cells, the current cell will change.

Filling values in cells

The cells are the locations where we enter values. Spreadsheets are primarily used for mathematical computations, but numbers would need text to state what they mean. So, spreadsheets allow two kinds of values for every cell: numbers and text.

A cell containing numbers can only contain any combination of digits between 0 to 9. Let's say that we enter the number 1200 in cell B2. To enter a value in a cell, place the cursor on the cell, enter the number, and then press the *Enter* key. The Microsoft Excel sheet looks as shown in *figure A1.2*:

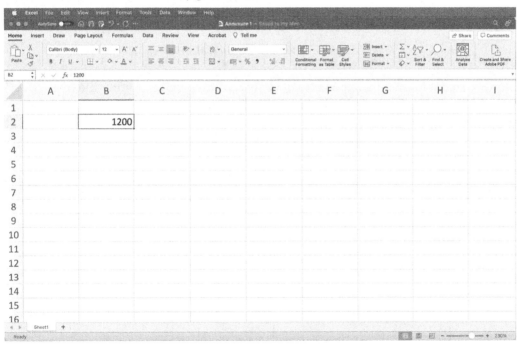

Figure A1.2: *A value of 1200 entered in cell B2*

Place the cursor on cell B2 and look at the top left corner below the menu. You will see that the current cell is B2, and it is stated that the value in cell B2 is 1200.

Let's say that 1200 is an amount we spend on buying milk coupons. We would like to make this clear to the reader, so we enter the text "**Milk Coupons**" in cell A2. To do so, place the cursor on cell A2, type the value "**Milk Coupon**," and press *Enter*. The Microsoft Excel sheet would look as shown in *figure A1.3*:

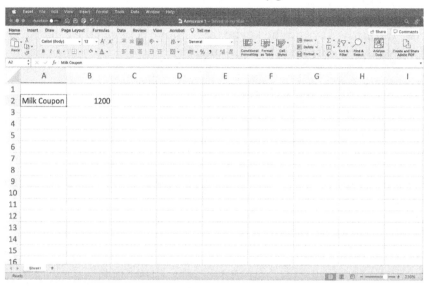

Figure A1.3: *The text "Milk Coupon" entered in cell A2*

Now, we want to add the expense of 3000 toward the maid. So, enter the text *"Maid"* in cell A3 and the number 3000 in cell B3. The Microsoft Excel sheet would look as illustrated in *figure A1.4*:

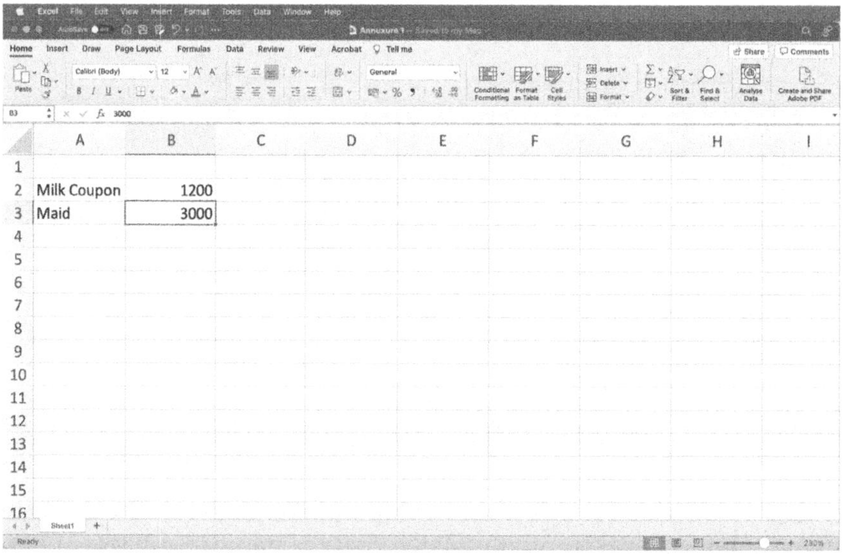

Figure A1.4: *The text "Maid" entered in cell A3, and the number 3000 entered in cell B3*

Now, let's enter the following in our sheet:

1. Driver's salary – 16000

2. House maintenance – 4000

3. Newspaper – 500

4. Electricity bill – 3500

5. Medicines – 6000

Enter the following values in the cells, as shown in *table A1.1*:

Cell	Entry	Cell	Entry
A4	Driver's Salary	B4	16000
A5	House Maintenance	B5	4000
A6	Newspaper	B6	500
A7	Electricity Bill	B7	3500
A8	Medicines	B8	6000

Table A1.1: *Values to enter in the Microsoft Excel sheet for the other expenses*

Our Microsoft Excel sheet would look as shown in *figure A1.5*:

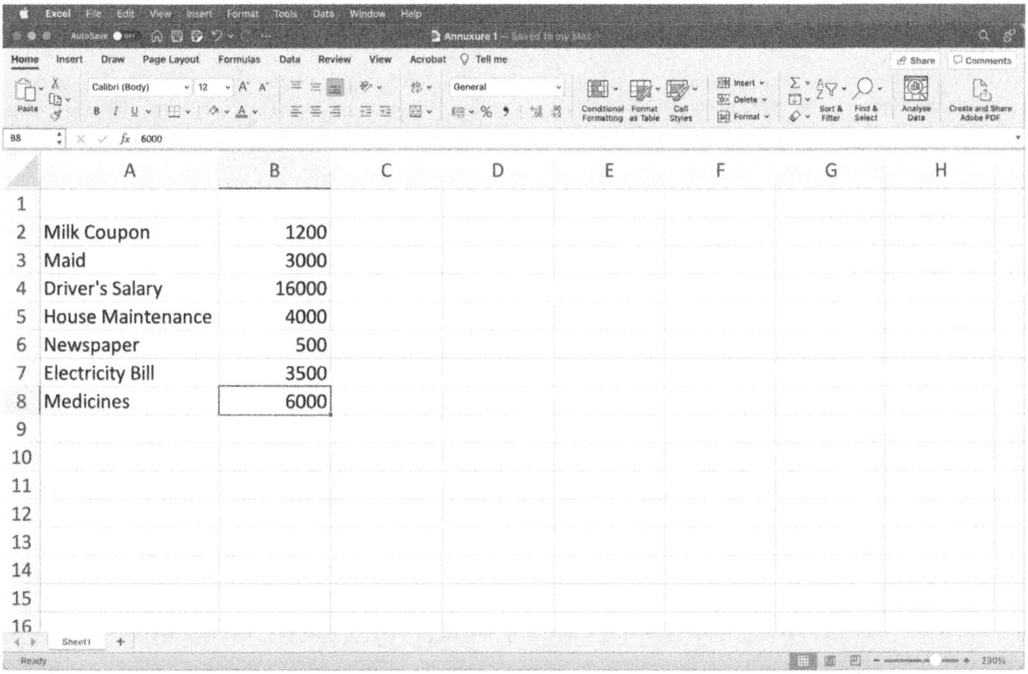

Figure A1.5: *Microsoft Excel sheet after entering the remaining expenses*

You can see that we have entered the expense head in column A and the associated amounts in column B. So, we would like to put a heading to make this clear. Enter the values as shown in *table A1.2* in the Microsoft Excel sheet:

Cell	Entry	Cell	Entry
A1	Expense Head	B1	Amount in Rs.

Table A1.2: *Adding title for the columns*

Now, we would like the heading in cells A1 and B1 to be in *bold* so that they can be distinguished for the remaining entries in the Microsoft Excel sheet. To do this, look at the top of the Microsoft Excel window as shown in *figure A1.5*. Note that there are some options with a green underline (Home, Insert, Draw, etc.) below the green bar. All these words are the tabs for invoking different features in Microsoft Excel. If you click on the different tabs, you will see that the options below them change. Now, see that there is a **B** option available under Home. The contents of cell A1 will be displayed in bold if you select cell A1 and click on the **B** button. We can do the same for cell B1 as well.

The Microsoft Excel sheet will look as shown in *figure A1.6*:

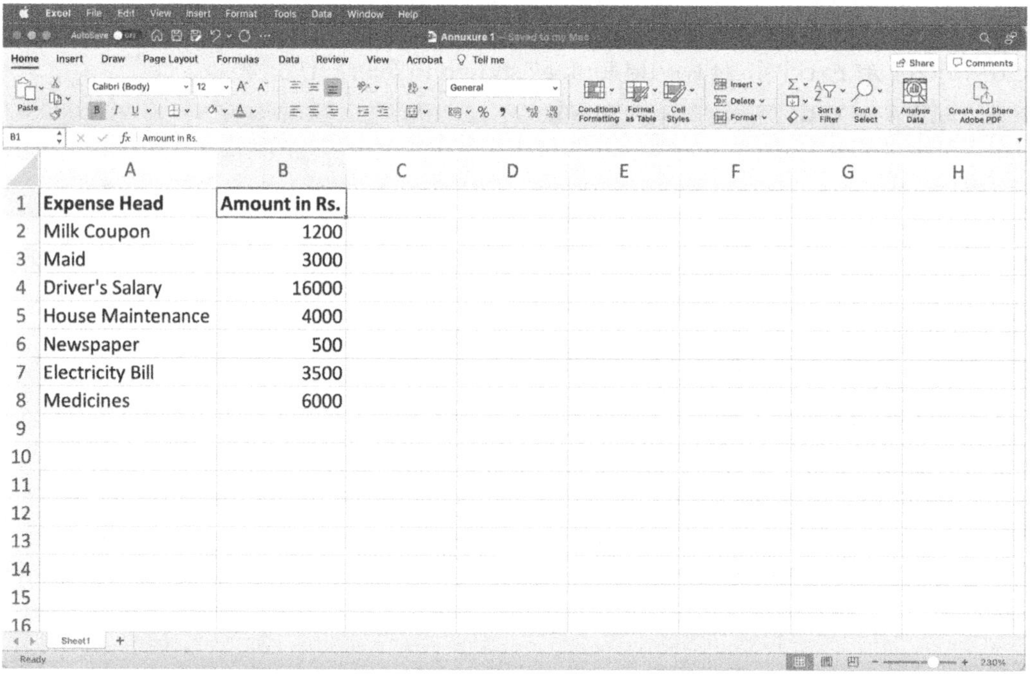

Figure A1.6: *Microsoft Excel sheet after adding header for columns A and B*

Using formula

The main purpose of spreadsheets is to do computations for us. This is accomplished by using formulas in spreadsheets. Just like we enter text and numbers in a cell, we can enter formulas as well. We just type the text or number in the cell to enter text or number, but we must start the cell entry with an equal (=) sign to enter a formula in a cell. Let's understand this with an example.

Now that we have our expenses, let's calculate our total expenses. Total expenses would be the sum of all our individual expenses. Let's get Microsoft Excel to do this work for us instead of adding these numbers ourselves. We will calculate the total expenses in cell B10, so enter the formula shown in *table A1.3* in cell B10:

Cell	Entry	Cell	Entry
A10	Total Expense	B10	=B2+B3+B4+B5+B6+B7+B8

Table A1.3: Formula to calculate the total expenses

Our Microsoft Excel sheet would look as shown in *figure A1.7*:

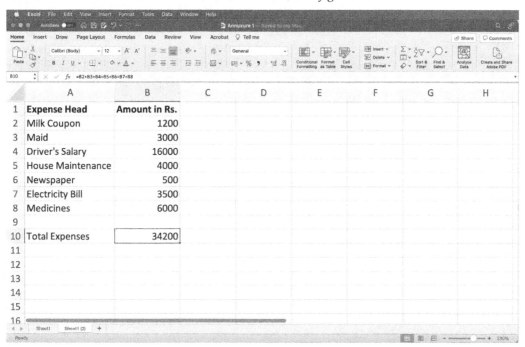

Figure A1.7: The Microsoft Excel sheet after entering the formula to calculate the total expenses

Note that cell B10 contains a formula, but the cell displays the result of the calculation.

If a formula is entered in a cell, Microsoft Excel will recalculate the formula whenever any of the values in the cell associated with the formula changes. Let's try this. Enter values in the cells as shown in *table A1.4*:

Cell	Entry	Cell	Entry
B2	1400	B6	600
B7	4000	B8	5000

Table A1.4: Formula to enter to calculate the total expenses

The updated Microsoft Excel sheet will look as shown in the *figure A1.8*:

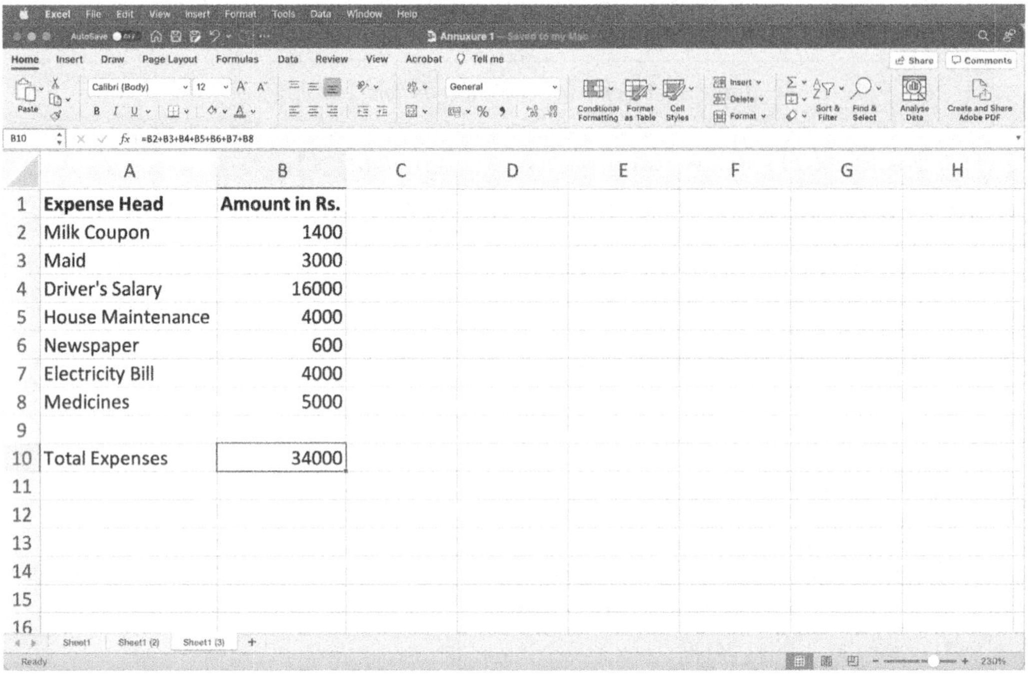

Figure A1.8: Microsoft Excel sheet after changing some of the expenses

Note that the formula in cell B10 was not changed, but Microsoft Excel computed the total expenses as per the changed values for the individual expenses.

Using Microsoft Excel built-in functions

You would have noticed that we had to refer to several cells (all the cells containing the individual expenses) when we were entering the formula to calculate the total expenses. Normally, we would have several cells involved in calculations, so it can be cumbersome to enter the formula, as we have seen so far. Microsoft Excel has several built-in functions to make this easy. In fact, Microsoft Excel has so many built-in functions, a book could be written about them. So, we will only discuss how to enter a formula, and we leave it to you to explore the functions available in Microsoft Excel.

We need to sum the values in cells B2 through B8 to calculate the total expenses. Now, cells B2 through B8 are contiguous cells, so we could refer to these cells as B2:B8. A colon (:) in between two cells means that the intermediate cells also need consideration. Next, Microsoft Excel provides a function to calculate the sum of a set of cells—SUM. So, we enter the formula shown in *table A1.5* to calculate the total expenses in cell B11:

Cell	Entry
B11	=SUM(B2:B8)

Table A1.5: *Formula to calculate the total expenses using Microsoft Excel built-in function*

Our Microsoft Excel sheet would look as shown in *figure A1.9*:

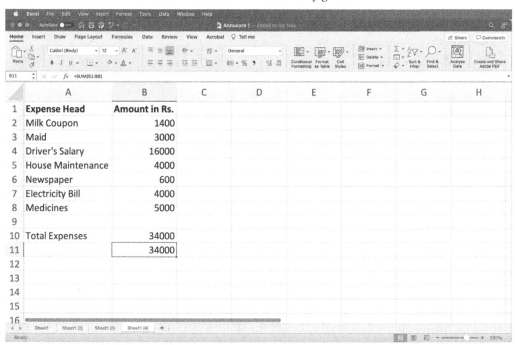

Figure A1.9: *Using the built-in function SUM to calculate the total expenses in cell B11*

Relative addressing

Let's consider that the amounts we entered in column B are the budgeted figures. Now, let's enter the actual expenses for January in column D, as shown in *table A1.6*:

Cell	Entry	Cell	Entry
D1	January	D5	4000
D2	1200	D6	450
D3	3000	D7	3421
D4	16000	D8	2375

Table A1.6: *Values to enter for actual expenses in January*

The Microsoft Excel sheet will look as shown in *figure A1.10*:

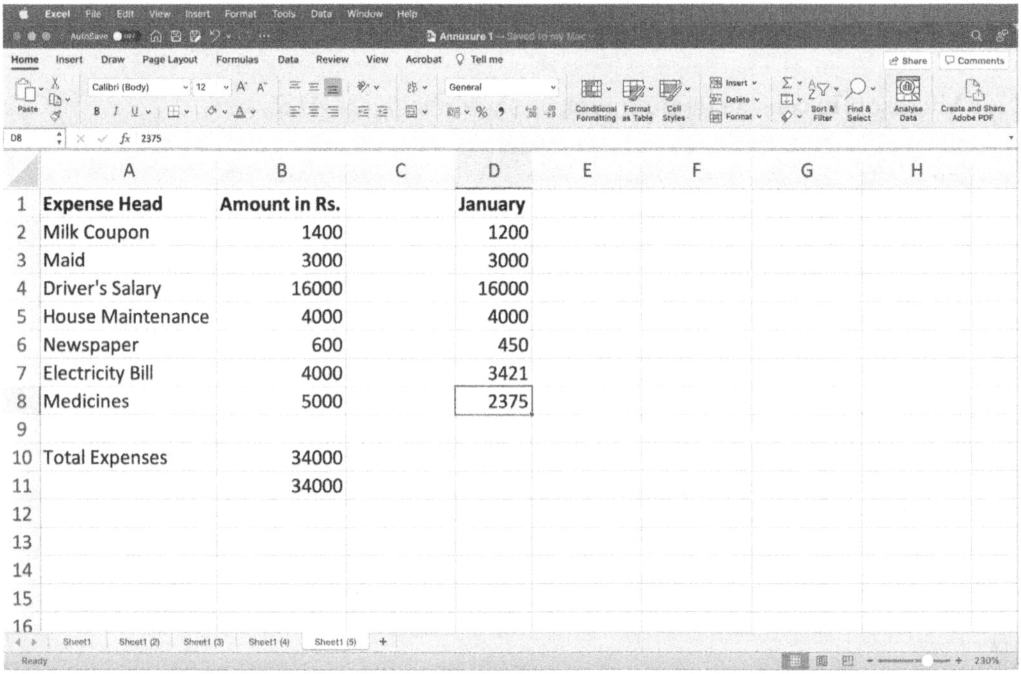

Figure A1.10: *Microsoft Excel sheet after entering the actual expenses in January*

Now, we would like to calculate the total expenses in the month of January in cell D10 and D11 (we will write the formula without using any Microsoft Excel built-in function in cell D10 and using Microsoft Excel built-in function in cell D11).

One way of doing this is to enter the formula, as we have already discussed. However, there is a much easier way in Microsoft Excel. The formula to calculate the total expenses for January is identical to the formula we used in cells B10 and B11, except that the formula in cells B10 and B11 refers to the cells in column B and we need the new formula to refer to column D. So, we will just copy the formula in cells B10 and B11 and paste it in cells D10 and D11, respectively.

To copy the value in cell B10, place the cursor on the cell and (under the **Home** menu options) click on the **Copy** button:

Figure A1.11: *Copy button*

To paste the value in cell D10, place the cursor on the cell and (under the **Home** menu options) click on the **Paste** button:

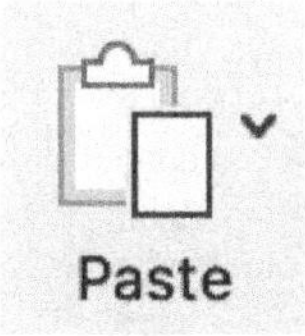

Figure A1.12: *Paste button*

The Microsoft Excel sheet will look as shown in *figure A1.13*:

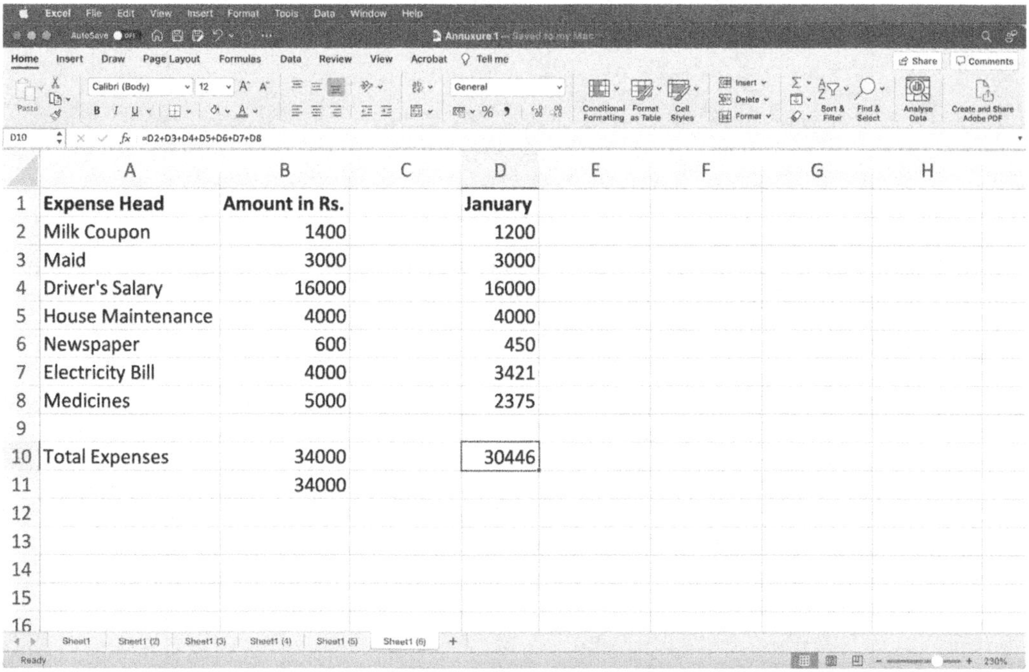

	A	B	C	D	E	F	G	H
1	Expense Head	Amount in Rs.		January				
2	Milk Coupon	1400		1200				
3	Maid	3000		3000				
4	Driver's Salary	16000		16000				
5	House Maintenance	4000		4000				
6	Newspaper	600		450				
7	Electricity Bill	4000		3421				
8	Medicines	5000		2375				
9								
10	Total Expenses	34000		30446				
11		34000						
12								
13								
14								
15								
16								

Figure A1.13: *Microsoft Excel sheet after copying the formula from cell B10 to cell D10*

Note that the formula in cell D10 is =D2+D3+D4+D5+D6+D7+D8. However, the formula we copied from cell B10 is =B2+B3+B4+B5+B6+B7+B8. This is because Microsoft Excel, by default, uses **relative addressing**. So, the formula in cell B10 is referring to cells that are 9 rows above it in the same column, 8 rows above it in the same column, and so on. So, it does the same when this formula is copied to cell D10.

Similarly, copy and paste the formula in cell B11 to cell D11. Our Microsoft Excel sheet will look as shown in *figure A1.14*:

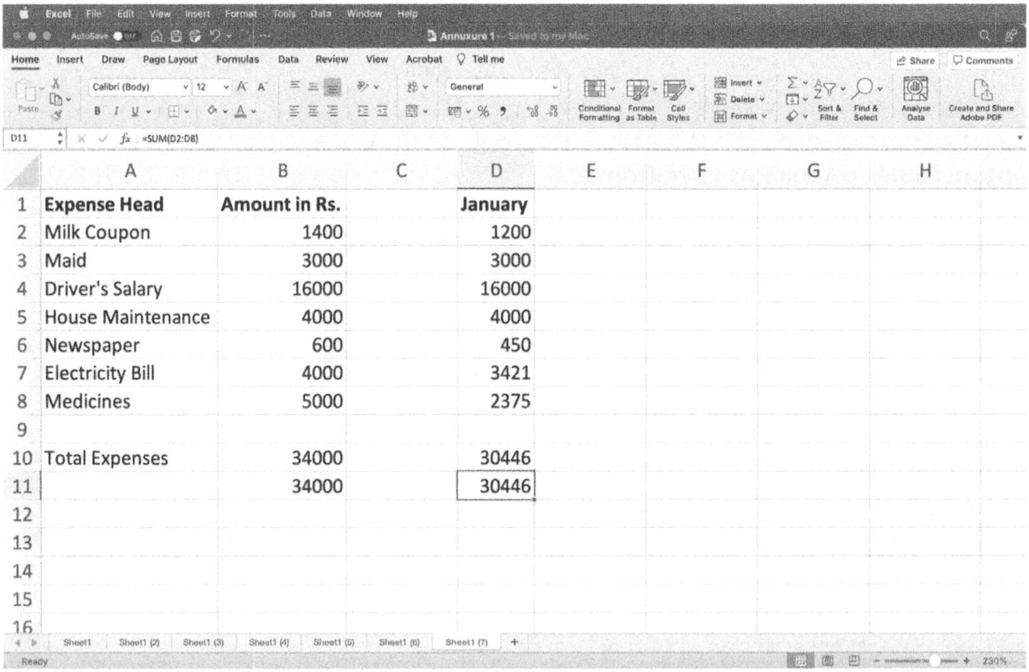

Figure A1.14: Formula in cell B11 copied to cell D11

Now, let's calculate how much we saved in January against our budget. To calculate the savings in Milk Coupons, we can subtract the value in cell D2 from the value in cell B2. So, make the entries shown in *table A1.7*:

Cell	Entry	Cell	Entry
E1	Savings	E2	=B2-D2

Table A1.7: Formula to calculate the savings in Milk Coupons in January against the budget

The Microsoft Excel sheet will look as shown in *figure A1.15*:

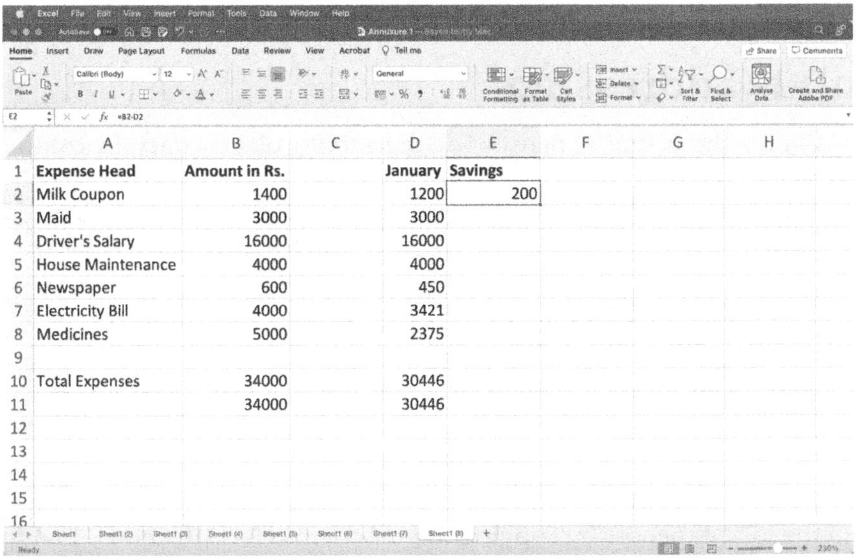

Figure A1.15: *Formula to calculate the savings in January for Milk Coupons against the budget*

Let's calculate the savings for the other expense heads; the formula would be identical. So, we can just copy and paste the formula in cell E2 to cells E3, E4, E5, E6, E7, and E8. To do this, place the cursor on cell E2 and click on **Copy**. Then, highlight cell E3 through E8 and click on **Paste**. The Microsoft Excel sheet will look as shown in *figure A1.16*:

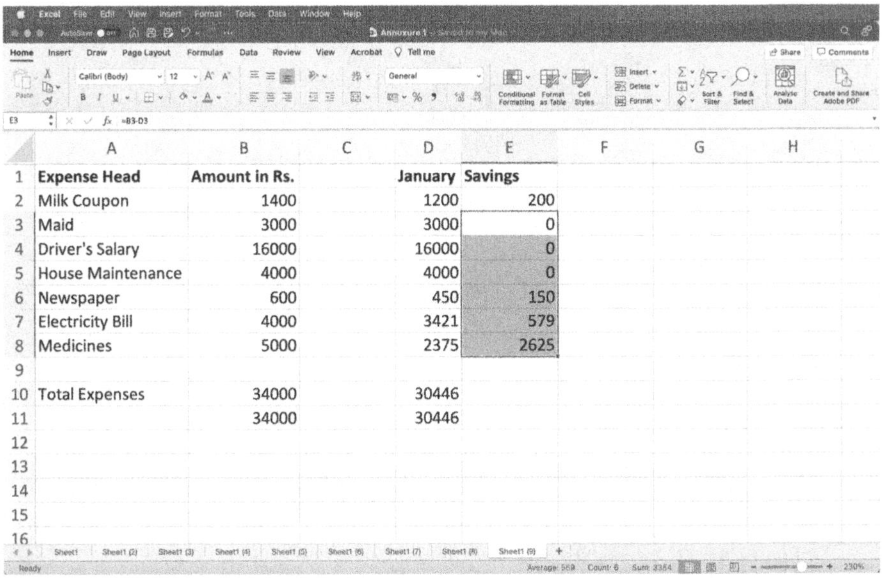

Figure A1.16: *Savings calculated for the remaining expenses*

Change the values for some of the expenses in January and see what happens. All the calculations should be refreshed.

Absolute addressing

Now, let's enter the actual expenses for the month of February in column G, as shown in *table A1.8*:

Cell	Entry	Cell	Entry
G1	February	G5	4000
G2	1300	G6	500
G3	3000	G7	3441
G4	16000	G8	3879

Table A1.8: Values to enter for actual expenses in February

Calculate the total expenses by copying the values in cells D10 and D11 and pasting them in cells G10 and G11, respectively.

The Microsoft Excel sheet will look as shown here:

	A	B	C	D	E	F	G	H	I
1	Expense Head	Amount in Rs.		January	Savings		February		
2	Milk Coupon	1400		1200	200		1300		
3	Maid	3000		3000	0		3000		
4	Driver's Salary	16000		16000	0		16000		
5	House Maintenance	4000		4000	0		4000		
6	Newspaper	600		450	150		500		
7	Electricity Bill	4000		3421	579		3441		
8	Medicines	5000		2375	2625		3879		
9									
10	Total Expenses	34000		30446			32120		
11		34000		30446			32120		
12									
13									
14									
15									
16									

Figure A1.17: Microsoft Excel sheet after entering the expenses for February

Now, let's calculate the savings in the month of February against the budget in column H. To calculate the savings in February, we must subtract the expenses in February mentioned in column G from the budgeted amount in column B. This is like the calculations we performed for the month of January. So, can we just copy and paste the formula for January to calculate the savings for February? Let's try this.

So, we copy and paste the formula from cells E2 through E8 to cells H2 to H8. Highlight cells E2 through E8 and click on **Copy** to do this. Then, highlight cells H2 through H8 and click on **Paste**. The Microsoft Excel sheet will look as shown in *figure A1.18*.

Note: We can also copy and paste the formula from cell E2 to cells H2 through H8 to get the same result. Place the cursor on cell E2 and click on Copy to do this. Then, highlight cells H2 through H8 and click on Paste.

	A	B	C	D	E	F	G	H	I
1	Expense Head	Amount in Rs.		January	Savings		February	Savings	
2	Milk Coupon	1400		1200	200		1300	-1100	
3	Maid	3000		3000	0		3000	-3000	
4	Driver's Salary	16000		16000	0		16000	-16000	
5	House Maintenance	4000		4000	0		4000	-4000	
6	Newspaper	600		450	150		500	-350	
7	Electricity Bill	4000		3421	579		3441	-2862	
8	Medicines	5000		2375	2625		3879	-1254	
9									
10	Total Expenses	34000		30446			32120		
11		34000		30446			32120		
12									
13									
14									
15									
16									

Figure A1.18: Copying the formula in cells E2 through E8 in cells H2 through H8

We see that the calculations are not correct. Note that the formula in cell H2 is =E2-G2 instead of =B2-G2. This is because of relative addressing.

We want the expense to always be subtracted from the budget in column B, so we need to anchor column B. To anchor a column, we add dollar ($) in front of the column reference of a cell. So, $B2 would mean that column B of cell B2 is anchored. Column B would not change when any formula involving cell B is copied, because of relative address. When we anchor a cell reference, we say that we are using **Absolute Addressing**. Let's try this.

Enter the formula shown in *table A1.9* in cell E2:

Cell	Entry
E2	=$B2-D2

Table A1.9: Formula for cell E2 with absolute addressing

The Microsoft Excel sheet would look as shown in *figure A1.19*. Note the formula in cell E2:

	A	B	C	D	E	F	G	H	I
1	Expense Head	Amount in Rs.		January	Savings		February	Savings	
2	Milk Coupon	1400		1200	200		1300	-1100	
3	Maid	3000		3000	0		3000	-3000	
4	Driver's Salary	16000		16000	0		16000	-16000	
5	House Maintenance	4000		4000	0		4000	-4000	
6	Newspaper	600		450	150		500	-350	
7	Electricity Bill	4000		3421	579		3441	-2862	
8	Medicines	5000		2375	2625		3879	-1254	
9									
10	Total Expenses	34000		30446			32120		
11		34000		30446			32120		
12									
13									
14									
15									
16									

Figure A1.19: Formula for cell E2 changed to use absolute addressing

Now, copy and paste the formula in cell E2 to cells E3 through E8. You will note that the formula in cells E3 to E8 is as shown in *table A1.10*:

Cell	Entry	Cell	Entry
		E5	=$B5-D5
E2	=$B2-D2	E6	=$B6-D6
E3	=$B3-D3	E7	=$B7-D7
E4	=$B4-D4	E8	=$B8-D8

Table A1.10: Formula in cells E3 through E8 after using absolute addressing in cell E2

Now, copy and paste the formula in cell E2 to cells H2 through H8. You will notice that the formula is as shown in *table A1.11*:

Cell	Entry	Cell	Entry
		H5	=$B5-G5
H2	=$B2-G2	H6	=$B6-G6
H3	=$B3-G3	H7	=$B7-G7
H4	=$B4-G4	H8	=$B8-G8

Table A1.11: *Formula in cell E3 through E8 after using absolute addressing in cell E2*

The Microsoft Excel sheet will look as shown in *figure A1.20*:

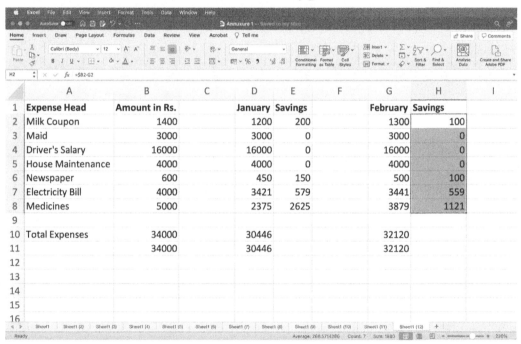

Figure A1.20: *Savings calculated for February*

Annexure 2

So far, we have discussed techniques for reducing a project's duration by converting the requirement into a linear programming problem. There are circumstances in a project where we may need to consider other methods for reducing the project duration before we can apply techniques of solving linear programming problems. We will discuss two such techniques in this annexure.

As it would have become clear by now, we can apply these techniques before or after converting our problem for crashing a project to a linear programming problem.

Structure

We will discuss the following topics in this chapter:

- Laddering
- Minimum Slack Rule

Objectives

After studying this unit, you should be able to understand the concepts of **Laddering** and **Minimum Slack Rule**.

Laddering

So far, we have seen how to crash a project by optimizing the duration of tasks based on what is possible in terms of reducing the duration of tasks. However, we can also reduce the duration of a project by reorganizing the tasks. One scientific way to accomplish this is by using a technique called **Laddering**.

Laddering is a technique where we break down certain tasks into smaller units and try to fit them into the project plan. Laddering is possible if an activity can be broken down into two or more sub-activities, and a succeeding activity is similarly broken down into the same number of sub-activities as its predecessor.

The important aspect to note is that we need to identify an activity that can be broken into smaller units. There are many such activities in a project; for example, we can break almost every activity in a software development project into smaller components. For example, instead of conducting the complete design of the product as a single activity, we can break it down into multiple activities of design.

Let's take a practical example. While developing software for a hospital, we broke down the project into three phases. In the first phase, we computerized all the departments that contributed to the generation of a bill for the patients. So, in the first phase, we computerized the admission department, wards, operation theaters, pharmacy, and laboratories. In the second phase, we computerized the ancillary departments, including kitchen, laundry, **Out-Patient Department (OPD)**, nephrology, and cardiology. In the third phase, we computerized the financial accounting system, the medical records system, and such.

> **Note:** The out-patient department, nephrology department, cardiology department, and other such departments also account for billing. However, these billing activities can be isolated from the billing for the in-patients. The main billing activity in a hospital is for the in-patients who spend a day or more in the hospital and consume activities across multiple departments. In contrast, the out-patients interact with a particular department of the hospital, and a bill is generated for that interaction.

So, we had broken down the project activities into three components. In each phase, we took up the work of requirement analysis, design, development, and so on module by module. Essentially, the activity of requirement analysis was broken down to requirement analysis for the admission department, requirement analysis for wards, requirement analysis for pharmacy, and such.

The second requirement for laddering is that we must also find a subsequent task to the task identified for decomposition, which can be broken down into the same number of sub tasks as the main task. So, if we consider our example, when we break the task of requirement analysis into components for each module, we can do the same for the design task. Now, the design task follows the requirement analysis task, so when we do the requirement analysis for the admission department, we will follow it up with the design of the system for the admission department. Similarly, we will follow up this technique for the rest of the modules.

Now, this may seem a routine mechanism for the practitioners of Agile methodology. The basic essence of adopting agile methodology is that we break down the project into smaller units and conduct the complete lifecycle for each of the units before proceeding to the next. Let's see how this can help us reduce the duration of the project.

Let's consider the project schedule in *figure A2.1* to understand the mechanism of laddering:

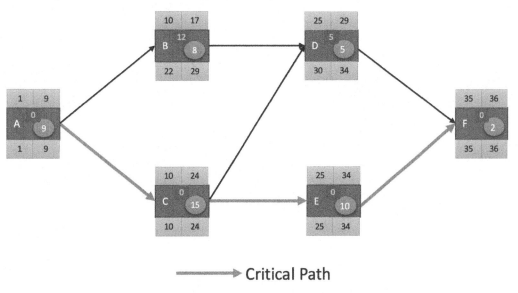

Figure A2.1: Original project plan before applying laddering

We can see that activities A and C are subsequent activities, so we will consider these two activities for laddering.

Note: The important aspect to note is that we must pick two activities on the critical path for laddering.

Let's say that we break activity A into two activities: A1 and A2. Now, activity A takes a duration of 9 units. Let's say that we break activity A such that activity A1 takes 5 units and activity A2 takes 4 units. So, we have ensured that the overall duration of activity A is the same.

Similarly, we will break activity C into activities C1 and C2. Activity C takes 15 days, so we will break activity C such that activity C1 takes 10 days and activity C2 takes 5 days. We have, again, ensured that the overall duration of C is the same.

We will conduct activity A2 after activity A1. From *figure A2.1*, we can see the need to conduct activity B after activity A, so we will conduct activity B after activity A2.

Similarly, we will conduct activity C2 after activity C1. From *figure A2.1*, we can see that activities D and E need to be conducted after activity C. So, we will conduct activities D and E after activity C2.

So, we get the project network as shown in *figure A2.2*:

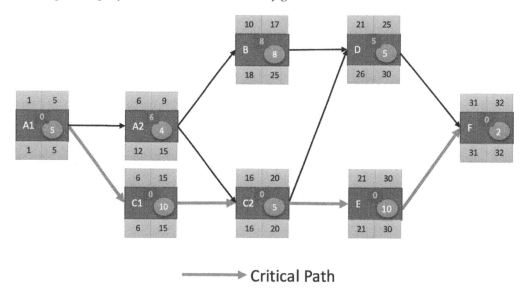

➡ Critical Path

Figure A2.2: Project network after laddering

Note that the project duration in *figure A2.1* was 36 units. The project duration after laddering (as shown in *figure A2.2*) is 32 units, so we have reduced the project duration by 4 units after laddering.

Minimum slack rule

Now, let's look at another aspect of project scheduling. All projects need resources to accomplish the tasks. So far, we have been discussing project scheduling assuming that all the required resources are available as per our planning. However, this may not be the case all the time. In any kind of project, we have several constraints related to resources. Let's understand how to schedule a project under resource constraints taking the example of a software development project.

Let's consider a project schedule as shown in *figure A2.3*:

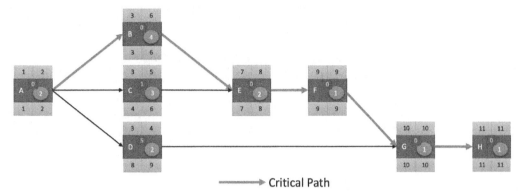

Figure A2.3: *Example project network*

We get the following when we plant the project schedule in *figure A2.3*:

	A	B	C	D	E	F	G	H
1	**Activity**	**Duration (weeks)**	**Predecessor**	**ES**	**EF**	**LS**	**LF**	**Slope**
2	A	2		1	2	1	2	0
3	B	4	A	3	6	3	6	0
4	C	3	A	3	5	4	6	1
5	D	2	A	3	4	8	9	5
6	E	2	B,C	7	8	7	8	0
7	F	1	E	9	9	9	9	0
8	G	1	D,F	10	10	10	10	0
9	H	1	G	11	11	11	11	0

Figure A2.4: *Project schedule shown in figure A2.3 planted on a Microsoft Excel sheet*

We can see that the project in figures A2.3 and A2.4 is scheduled to complete in 11 weeks. Now, let's add resources to perform the tasks. Let's say that resource R0 will carry out task A, resource R1 will carry out tasks B, C, and D, resource R2 will perform tasks E and H, resource R3 will perform task F, and resource R4 will perform task G. After allocating the resources, the project schedule is as shown in *figure A2.5*:

	A	B	C	D	E	F	G	H	I
1	Activity	Duration (weeks)	Predecessor	ES	EF	LS	LF	Slope	Resource
2	A	2		1	2	1	2	0	R0
3	B	4	A	3	6	3	6	0	R1
4	C	3	A	3	5	4	6	1	R1
5	D	2	A	3	4	8	9	5	R1
6	E	2	B,C	7	8	7	8	0	R2
7	F	1	E	9	9	9	9	0	R3
8	G	1	D,F	10	10	10	10	0	R4
9	H	1	G	11	11	11	11	0	R2

Figure A2.5: Project schedule after adding resources to tasks

We see that resource R1 is expected to simultaneously work on tasks B, C, and D. This is clearly not possible. Let's say that we do not find any other resource to help this situation, so the only option is that we carry out tasks B, C, and D one after the other.

Now, the question is, "which task out of tasks B, C, and D should resource R1 take up first, second, and third. This is where we apply the minimum slack rule. We see that the slack of task B is 0, the slack of task C is 1, and the slack of task D is 5. So, according to the minimum slack rule, resource R1 should perform task B first, followed by task C and D.

If we apply the minimum slack rule and rearrange the tasks, the project network will be as shown in *figure A2.6*:

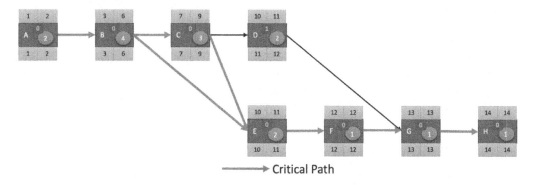

Figure A2.6: Altered project schedule after applying minimum slack rule

Under the constraint posed by the fact that resource R1 should perform tasks B, C, and D, the minimum duration in which we can complete the project is 14 weeks, as shown in *figure A2.6.*

Let's see whether we get the project schedule with the minimum duration by applying the minimum slack rule. Let's say that we have resource R1 perform task C first, then task D, followed by task B. The project schedule would be as shown in *figure A2.7*:

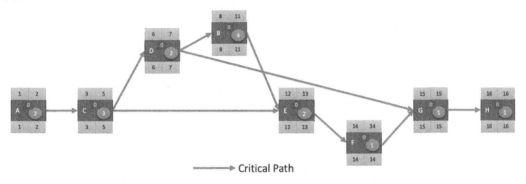

Figure A2.7: *Project schedule not applying minimum slack rule*

Note that the project duration is 16 weeks by not applying the minimum slack rule. This is more than the duration of 14 weeks that we got by applying the minimum slack rule.

Note: The minimum slack rule should be applied whenever we have a situation where we need to decide between two or more tasks to break scheduling contention.

Index

Made in United States
North Haven, CT
14 May 2022